H. C. Keller is a Material Handling Consultant whose clients include national manufacturing companies, equipment builders, and systems consultants. He was previously Vice President, Technical Services, of the Lamson Corporation. Mr. Keller is a Fellow of the American Society of Mechanical Engineers, and has served as Chairman of the Society's Materials Handling Division and of the Technical Committee of the Conveyor Equipment Manufacturers Association. His articles have appeared in several of the professional journals, including *Factory* and *Modern Materials Handling*, and he contributed to the coverage of package conveyors, unit handling, and positioning equipment in the *Materials Handling Handbook*, published by The Ronald Press Company.

UNIT-LOAD AND PACKAGE
CONVEYORS

APPLICATION AND DESIGN

H. C. KELLER
MATERIAL HANDLING CONSULTANT

THE RONALD PRESS COMPANY • NEW YORK

Library of Congress Catalog Card Number: 66–21856

PRINTED IN THE UNITED STATES OF AMERICA

Preface

The purpose of this book is to bring together, in a single working reference, current knowledge and practice in the design and application of unit-load and package conveyors.

Recommendations and formulae are based on the more common problems and operating conditions. It is, of course, impossible to anticipate all the factors that may be encountered in analyzing a particular material-handling problem. Apparently minor differences in otherwise identical cartons of the same size and weight may demand different conveyor systems. Variation in such factors as handling speed and the presence or absence of heat or air conditioning in assembly or storage areas may indicate entirely different equipment for handling a given product. Appropriate modification in the recommended design procedures and system elements will therefore be necessary for meeting special requirements.

The author's extensive experience with unit-load conveyors includes much experimentation and many errors. It is his hope that the fruit of this experience, as set forth here, may reduce the necessity for trial-and-error methods and provide other designers with useful tools for reaching quick solutions to their problems.

H. C. Keller

De Witt, New York
January, 1967

Contents

UNIT-LOAD AND PACKAGE

CONVEYORS

APPLICATION AND DESIGN

1

Historical Background

Over 2,000 years ago, the Babylonians used the "Chain of Pots" to elevate water to the Hanging Gardens of Semiramis. Almost 200 years ago, Oliver Evans designed and built belt conveyors and bucket elevators. He described his belt conveyor as ". . . an endless strap of thin flexible leather, canvas, etc. revolving over two pulleys and riding in a trough one end of which is lower than the other. The grain or meal falls from the elevator onto the belt and by its own gravity and fall sets the machine in motion. This machine moves on the principles of an overshot waterwheel." This "machine" (belt conveyor) was an improvement over the screw conveyor for handling grains, seeds, etc., in granaries because of its greater capacity. The friction between the sliding belt and trough, however, shortened the life of the belting. This shortcoming was overcome by the introduction of rolls or idlers to support the moving belt.

In the late 1800's, William Lamson operated a small dry goods store. On Saturdays, business was so good that it was necessary to employ clerks to help serve the customers. After each sale the clerks had to push their way through the aisles to reach the cash drawer to make change. To avoid this confusion Lamson cut croquet balls in half, hollowed out the halves, and finally fitted them with grooved locks so that they could be screwed together again. The balls, with the customers' money, then were placed in sloping troughs and gravitated to a cashier. Another return trough permitted the balls to be returned to the clerks with the customers' change. Later, balls of various diameters were used and the return trough fitted with "drop-out" slots so that one trough could serve several clerk stations.

These few examples of early ingenuity are given to illustrate the fact that the advantages of material-handling equipment have been recognized for centuries. However, progress in this field was slow until the turn of the present century, when the introduction of electrical power, with its resultant effect on the surge of technological improvements, plus

3

the need for increased production speeded the design and use of many types of material-handling equipment.

Early conveyors were gravity operated or manually propelled, for example, the bucket elevators used to irrigate farmlands. They were often powered by men treading paddle wheels. With electric motors another problem was introduced. The speed reduction from the motor rotor to the drive shaft of the conveyor was solved by means of trains of flat belt drives or spur gear reductions. V-belt drives and compact gear reducers followed. A few decades ago this author saw a belt conveyor drive in service in New York City that employed three spur gear reductions and finally a flat belt drive to the motor. He saw also a vertical conveyor in another city handling sacks of flour with a flat belt drive to the motor. This installation left a lasting impression because the belt slipped off the pulleys while several bags were being raised. The resulting drop of the cars on the conveyor with the broken bags spilling the flour into the air presented a fire hazard until the dust had settled and had been cleared away.

In the beginning of this century all conveyor shafts operated in sleeve bearings lined with babbitt, bronze, etc., requiring elaborate and costly millwrighting to avoid excessive friction and wear. The shafts of idler or carrying rolls on belt conveyors likewise operated in sleeve bearings or bushings. Anti-friction ball and roller bearings for pulley and sprocket shafts and anti-friction bearings mounted in rollers with fixed shafts are a comparatively recent development. The rollers used in roller gravity conveyors have had a similar history.

In the last thirty years many new types of conveyors and industrial trucks have been developed; and, with the great strides that have been made in electrical control equipment in recent years, many sophisticated and fully automatic handling systems have been made possible. The near future will certainly bring advancements as great or greater than those made in the past few decades. Many conceptions, presently only dreams in the minds of material-handling men, will become practical, realistic installations.

2

Analyzing Equipment Needs

When raw material leaves the mine or wherever it originates, and is shipped to a processing plant, its cost is increased by the charge for transportation. After processing and shipping to a manufacturing plant or warehouse, another transporting or handling cost is added. All handling of the material in the manufacturing plant and shipping of the finished article to the user also add to the cost.

None of the handling moves adds to the value of the material to the ultimate user; all movement, however, does increase the cost of the item.

In many plants, where accurate studies have been made of handling costs, the results show that handling charges exceed the cost of processing the material into a usable article. Many systems of cost accounting are not detailed enough to give the true and complete material-handling cost. "Move" men are frequently charged to factory overhead; first cost and maintenance of material-handling equipment (cranes, industrial trucks, conveyors) are likewise buried in a general overhead account. Whatever the type of cost analysis used, we know that any reduction in the number of times the material is moved, in the distance to be traveled, in the time to make the move, or in the number of times the material is picked up or laid down will represent a savings in cost.

Design and Production

The first consideration in making an analysis of the cost of a product is not a breakdown of handling but a study of the design of the product and the method of producing it.

A design study may result in a change that will reduce the number of pieces going into the assembly. It is possible that the use of other materials will also contribute to a simpler arrangement where one new piece will replace two or more in the present design.

When we are satisfied that the design has been perfected, we can study the manufacturing procedure. Perhaps rearranging machine tools so that some movements can be reduced or even eliminated or combining operations on a modified or new tool will help cut down the number of moves.

Handling Economies

Only after we are satisfied that the design of the product and the method of producing it are perfected, are we ready to study the material-handling problem. One very important consideration in any study of handling methods is to look for and avoid manual lifting and tugging of any type. Much time is lost due to back injuries and hernia. Not only is this lost time costly in production interruptions, but the compensation insurance premium can be a big item of overall cost.

Every effort should be made to keep material flowing from operation to operation and to avoid the necessity of setting the material down or into a stock pile before picking it up again or of removing it from stock when the next operation is ready to receive it.

When it is necessary to make parts ahead and to stock them temporarily, try to place them into totes or containers or palletize them so that they can be handled in large units. Lift trucks can then be employed to raise the totes or pallets into storage bins or racks. In this way we utilize vertical storage and require only a minimum of floor space and travel time of the trucks.

It may be advisable to install gravity storage racks so that the totes can move ahead in the rack. In this way we are assured of "first in first out" flow when this is essential, and this also permits an orderly flow of truck traffic. Under certain conditions conveyors may be indicated to handle the totes in place of the trucks.

Conveyors can be used to move components from machine to machine with those parts on the conveyor acting as temporary storage to smooth out fluctuations in production and demand between the various machine operations.

Frequently, when machine tools are adjacent, a simple mechanical handling arm can remove a piece from one machine and place it into the next. Under some conditions an overhead crane will prove more practical than a mechanical arm or a conveyor.

Factors in Analysis

Many factors are studied by analysts to determine if material-handling equipment is needed in an operation or if up-dating of present equipment is needed. All analysts do not agree on the figures used, but they do agree that no one factor can be used in every case. The analyst must have or must obtain an intimate knowledge of the industry being studied to enable him to adjust the factors to suit the case.

LABOR

The first step is to determine the cost of material-handling labor. A list of material-handling personnel should include:

1. Conveyor loaders and unloaders, operators of powered and non-powered trucks (including any intraplant tractors or other trucks), crane operators (including riggers), and all labor used to form pallet loads.
2. Maintenance personnel employed in servicing material-handling equipment.
3. All labor assigned to receiving, storage, and shipping areas.

If the cost of the above labor is 20 per cent or more of the total cost of production, it generally indicates that there is room for improvement. It may be necessary to adjust the figure to fit a particular operation, but the 20 per cent figure is a good guide.

MACHINE UTILIZATION

In most industries, skilled labor, such as machine tool operators, spend some of their time in handling or waiting for materials. When these workers spend more than 10 per cent of their time in such unskilled efforts, a change in procedure should be considered. It may be that a simple mechanical aid will reduce handling time, while a rearrangement of the machine in relation to plant layout can reduce waiting time.

Loss in machining time may be caused by other than time lost in handling and/or waiting. It may be that a product requires a certain machining operation, but because of low volume poor utilization of the machine is realized.

Improper production planning can be another cause of a low utilization factor. Poor scheduling in lot sizes, requiring frequent setups, or the slow flow of paper work may be the cause. Faulty plant layout, requiring frequent backtracking of materials, could be another contributing factor.

MOTION ECONOMY

Unnecessary lifting and laying down of material often requires the skilled operator's time. The handling moves should not exceed 30 per cent of the total production operations. Production operations include the necessary handling of material into and out of position at the machine;

these moves cannot be charged to handling moves. Often a simple conveyor, providing "live" storage of parts between machine operations, will eliminate unnecessary handling as well as reduce time waiting for material.

STORAGE

If material must be temporarily stored between operations, be certain that the storage area permits full utilization of the space available. If storage is spread over a wide area or in disconnected spots in the plant, there may be excessive time lost in the movement of trucks or other handling devices. The use of air rights by employing storage racks and lift trucks could be the answer to improvement of storage operations.

OTHER FACTORS

There are many other factors that must be considered when evaluating the efficiency of an operation. One of these is the overall time cycle, i.e., the production hours in relation to the total elapsed time in the manufacturing plant. In many cases the ratio is necessarily very high, but all effort should be made to reduce it. Poor production control, inefficient plant layout, or improper handling equipment can all contribute to a high ratio.

All three factors given—20 per cent handling cost to total cost, 10 per cent skilled workers' time in unskilled work-handling motions, 30 per cent or more of total production motions—may all have to be modified in a particular case. As noted previously, a thorough knowledge of the industry is necessary to arrive at a reasonable decision. If the competitive picture is unfavorable, a review of the operation, using the factors suggested as guides, will help to pinpoint the areas where improvements are indicated.

3

Classes of Equipment

Cranes

In the general classification of cranes we can include the traveling overhead bridge type that operates on fixed rails with an operator in a control cab riding with the crane; the smaller bridge type where controls may be operated from the floor; the hoist mounted on a single rail with control from the floor through a pendant control panel or an operator in a cab suspended from the overhead rail; the jib crane and the manual operated or powered chain hoist.

Traveling bridge cranes are used outdoors in storage areas or indoors where heavy units or complete assemblies are hoisted and moved. In some cases the tracks extend from the plant into the yard so that material may be moved from outdoor storage to operations in the plant and returned to the yard for temporary storage between operations. Such arrangements are also used to move finished assemblies from inside the plant to shipping points outdoors.

These bridge cranes are also used to place heavy units into and to remove them from machine tools. The skilled operator can place the heavy piece accurately into the machine without the need for laborious pulling and tugging on the part of the floor man or the machine operator. An example of smooth and accurate handling is in a foundry where this type of crane frequently conveys a large ladle of molten metal over the molds while pouring ingots or castings. Two cranes are sometimes employed to operate in tandem when hoisting unusually large and bulky assemblies.

Important factors in efficient crane operation are the type of sling used to lift or hold the load, and the method of supporting the load to assure smooth and steady handling. This important task is the duty of a rigger who is a member of the crane crew.

The smaller and lighter-duty bridge crane is usually operated by the floor man using controls mounted on a pendant. It is used for moving units into and out of machine tools or lifting them onto pallets or skids for further movement by trucks or conveyors. The area served by this type of crane is normally confined to small sections of the factory to avoid excessive travel by the floor man.

A hoist mounted on a carriage operating on a single rail is made in two general types. One type has the hoisting motor and travel motor controls mounted on a pendant, and the movement then is controlled by an operator on the floor. Such a unit can be used in a manner similar to that previously described for the light-duty bridge crane. It also is used for placing units into storage and removing them from storage areas and storage racks.

The other type has a control cab mounted with the hoist mechanism and the entire unit is suspended from the single track. The most common utilization of this crane is in storage areas. At times the track is equipped with fork switches permitting the hoisting mechanism to be moved over any predetermined part of the storage area. Or, the track may have transverse sections that can move the hoist and cab in over the storage area. After a load has been picked up or discharged, the transverse section returns to the main track.

The jib crane is a hoist mounted on a stub rail that usually pivots on a fixed mast. This type of crane is normally located at a machine tool to effect transfer of heavy units between skids, pallets, or conveyors and the machine tool.

Manually operated or motor powered chain hoists can be suspended from a fixed point, or they may be mounted on a carriage that in turn is supported from a single track. Movement along this track is by manual effort against the suspended load.

A piece of allied equipment that is neither a true crane, elevator, or a lift truck is a hoist mechanism consisting of a car upon which totes, pallets, or skids are raised to and lowered from various storage rack levels. The structure can be suspended from an overhead track with parallel conductor bars supplying the electric power. The structure may extend to the floor where stabilizing guide tracks are installed. On occasion the main structure is supported on two tracks on the floor, and the top of the unit is usually extended to permit electrical contacts to engage power conductor bars.

An operator may ride with the hoisting mechanism to control the raising and lowering operations as well as the travel of the unit along the track. Many of these hoists, however, are automatically operated, and the unit is dispatched to a point along the track, elevated to the proper rack level; the car then moves to either side to place a load into or remove it from storage. Upon completion of its assigned task, the unit returns to the starting point. Some more sophisticated systems have the hoist place an item in stock and then remove another item from stock on its return trip. Various control systems are used to program the movement of the hoist along the track and the elevating mechanism.

Crane and Monorail manufacturers should be consulted to assist in selecting the type of equipment needed to meet a specific requirement.

Cranes vs. Trucks vs. Conveyors

It is perhaps best to interrupt our discussion on available material-handling equipment to cover a point that is frequently asked: "How can we determine whether cranes, trucks, or conveyors are the answer to our handling problem?" These three general types of equipment are not competitive. Each type serves a particular need and a careful analysis will indicate which should be used. In most operations a combination of two or all three types is needed to give an efficient integrated system.

On occasion, where transportation is the only requirement, the question of which general type should be used may arise. Generally, however, the distance to be traveled, the nature of the ground to be covered, the speed with which the transfer must be made, the capacity requirements, the nature of the product, etc., will indicate whether cranes, trucks, or conveyors are best suited to fill the need.

If, because of bulk, shape, or weight, it is decided to use a crane in the manufacturing area, any available time should be employed to have the crane convey the material through the plant. If, however, the crane is needed for a high percentage of its available time to lift and lower loads, then the load can be lowered onto the bed of a truck or onto a conveyor or pallet on the conveyor for transportation through the plant.

When the product is palletized, lift trucks can be used to remove the load from the palletizing station, transport it to a storage area, lift it to various levels in storage, or transport the load directly to the shipping dock.

If, however, the palletizing station is located at a remote point from storage or the shipping dock, or if it is located on another floor, then conveyors can be used to transport the pallet load, to raise or lower it to the proper floor level, and to bring it to a point where the lift truck can remove it, place it into storage, or spot it on the shipping dock.

The same combination of different types of handling equipment can be used for products that are not palletized. Examples are refrigerators, stoves, washing machines, television sets, etc., that are large enough to be handled in their individual shipping cartons or crates.

In almost every industrial operation there is need for all three types of equipment, and in many plants the handling operations are combined, necessitating connecting operations or special transfer devices between crane and truck, crane and conveyor, or truck and conveyor.

Industrial Trucks

The hand truck is probably the oldest form of material-handling equipment. Two-wheel trucks are used on loading and receiving docks, and they are frequently used to move items in warehouses and manufacturing plants.

The four-wheel truck can readily be adapted to mechanical propulsion. Motorized trucks are available in the "walkie" or the rider type. Tractors are used to haul "trains" of four-wheel trucks, permitting many trucks to be moved with one power unit and one rider or operator.

Tractor trains can be made to follow fixed paths automatically. Electronic control on the power unit follows a powered or magnetic strip in the floor, or "eyes" on the power unit scan a guideline and follow it. The train can be automatically halted and after loads have been removed or placed on the trucks, the train is again activated and travels until it reaches the next designated stopping point.

Automatic loaders and unloaders are available to place or remove unit loads, such as pallets, on or off the trucks when the tractor train stops at stations.

TOW SYSTEMS

Conveyor tow systems with a moving chain recessed in the floor or mounted overhead are frequently employed to move four-wheel trucks in a fixed path or circuit. Tow pins on the truck are dropped through a slot in the floor to engage the moving chain. Slings on the truck can be hooked into attachments on a moving overhead chain, or rigid masts on the trucks can be equipped with a telescopic upper section that is raised to engage hook attachments on the overhead chain.

Automatic disengagement of the truck from the moving chain at predetermined points makes the truck tow system ideal for many truck and rail terminal operations, for order picking and storage operations in warehouses, and in manufacturing plants for moving material between operations. Tow systems on different floors can be automatically linked by using special vertical conveyors to elevate or lower the trucks. The connections or transfers between the tow systems and the vertical conveyors are automatic, and the discharge code designating the point where the truck is to be disengaged is maintained.

Fig. 3–1. Hydraulically operated rams for coil handling on lift truck. (Courtesy Towmotor Corporation.)

The truck's destination can be coded in a control on the truck or on a convenient control panel fixed to the building structure. If the code is carried by the truck, a reader ahead of the diverting point triggers a diverter and the truck is deflected. If the code is set in a fixed panel, a memory device keeps record of the truck's progress and then triggers the diverting mechanism at the proper time.

The coding device on the truck may be entirely mechanical thereby eliminating electrical equipment. Generally the electrical coding device on the truck is more economical than the mechanical coding unit. However, the diverting mechanism on the electrical system is more expensive than the arrangement needed to divert a truck equipped with a mechanical coding device. Therefore, consideration of the number of trucks to be equipped with coders, the number of diverting points (sidings), and the probable maintenance cost will determine which system is the most economical for a particular installation.

The tow system with the moving chain located in the floor has the advantage of keeping the area above the conveyor path clear of all obstructions. The slot in the floor is only about one inch wide and so does

Fig. 3–2. Lift truck equipped with clamp handling paper rolls. (Courtesy Towmotor Corporation.)

not interfere with normal floor traffic. The cost of providing the necessary tunnels and pits in the floor for the conveyor may be more expensive than the cost of overhead structure needed to support the conveyor if installed above the floor. This is especially true if the installation is made in a plant already built. Also, the cost of changing the layout of the conveyor path after the original installation can be more expensive than a similar change in the layout of a conveyor with the tow chain installed overhead.

The overhead chain construction, however, requires that the moving chain be located low enough to permit operators readily to reach the moving hooks when they are engaging the slings towing the trucks. If rigid masts are supplied on the trucks, the moving chain can be located somewhat higher but the length or height of the mast cannot be so great as to throw the truck off balance when being engaged with the moving chain and while being towed around curves in the conveyor path. The

Fig. 3–3. Lift truck equipped with boat-handling forks. (Courtesy Towmotor Corporation.)

resulting low headroom under the overhead structure then can be objectionable, because it will interfere with loads on trucks normally crossing the path of the conveyor.

POWERED TRUCKS

Powered industrial trucks range from the simple rider type, designed to handle material in a horizontal plane, to units that elevate, revolve the load, position the load, etc., as well as transport it. The latter type of truck can be equipped with attachments suitable for handling almost any kind of load. In most cases fork-type attachments are used to handle pallets, skids, racks, or containers. The containers may handle bulk material. Some attachments are in the form of a scoop designed to lift, transport, and dump bulk material.

Other attachments are available for handling loads not normally palletized or skidded. Metal coils, cable reels, rolls of paper, bales of all kinds, pipes, drums, etc., are examples of loads that can be elevated, positioned, and/or rotated as well as transported.

Some units are designed to permit the operator to rise with an elevating platform. In addition to installation and maintenance work, such trucks are used to pick items for shipment from high storage racks or bins.

Fig. 3–4. Lift truck with scoop handling bulk material. (Courtesy Towmotor Corporation.)

The industrial truck is available with three general types of motive power: (1) the internal combustion engine, which may be fueled with gasoline, diesel, or liquefied petroleum gas; (2) electrically powered, with power received from storage batteries; (3) gas–electric, with an internal combustion engine driving a generator which supplies electric power.

Trucks designed to operate in confined quarters such as narrow aisles in storage areas, and equipped with crane hooks, and reach-type forks that can be extended under pallets and skids in storage racks, etc., are a few examples of special-purpose units available.

Manufacturers of these trucks should be consulted to assist in deciding the type of truck and the kind of power best suited to a particular operation.

Conveyors

In the general classification of conveyors there are many devices that are modifications of or combinations of the basic mediums used to convey material. The three natural mediums used are:

1. Gravity—slides, chutes, roller and wheel conveyors.
2. Air—pneumatic and vacuum systems.
3. Water—hydraulic conveyor systems.

The basic conveyor mediums are:

1. Roller conveyor—manual or gravity operated—and powered roller (live-roll).
2. Wheel conveyor—manual or gravity operated.
3. Chutes or slides—gravity operated.
4. Belt conveyor—horizontal, inclined, and vertical (bucket elevators).
5. Chain conveyor—slat, drag, overhead trolley, tow, en-masse, flight, pan, apron, verticals, bucket elevators, etc.
6. Cable conveyor—tramways, cableways, overhead trolley, verticals, etc.
7. Screw conveyors.

There are two major divisions of conveyor type: bulk material conveyors, and package or unit-load conveyors. Bulk conveyors are those employed to handle sand, gravel, ore, coal, ashes, cement, grains, flour, and almost any material that is not packaged, crated, or otherwise handled in unit loads. The package conveyors are those designed to handle small pieces weighing ounces to large units such as filled pallets, crates, or assemblies weighing tons. Included, of course, are the intermediate loads such as cartons, boxes, pans, and other types of totes.

Fig. 3–5. Belt conveyor handling bulk material to outdoor storage piles. (Courtesy Rex Chainbelt Inc.)

Many units such as belt conveyors, chain conveyors, pneumatic conveyors, etc., are used for both bulk and packaged material. Also, there are many conveyor accessories that are identified by the same name but used in connection with both bulk and package conveyors. It would be well to include in the material-handling library *Conveyor Terms and Definitions* (American Standard MH 4.1-1958), available from Conveyor Equipment Manufacturers Association, Washington, D.C. 20005.

A brief description of the major units used for bulk material conveying follows.

SLIDES OR CHUTES

Slides or chutes, both straight and spiral, are used to lower bulk material. They are made of metal, wood, and at times of plastic material. The latter is usually fiber glass. When made in spiral form, the most common purpose is to avoid damage to the material, which would occur if it were dropped into a storage silo or bin. The material flows down the spiral and, as the pile increases, it then flows over the outer side rim or guard to fill the storage area.

The chief use of slides is as connections—between conveyors, from conveyors to storage bins or processing machines, or for loading material from bins and machines to conveyors. The slides may be straight or combined with partial curves to effect transfers between units angled to any degree. When used as connections they are considered as an accessory and not as a major conveyor unit.

BELTS

The belt conveyor is the most widely used conveyor for handling bulk material because of its versatility. It has capacity for conveying a continuous stream of material at high speed over long distances. The belting has good abrasive resistance.

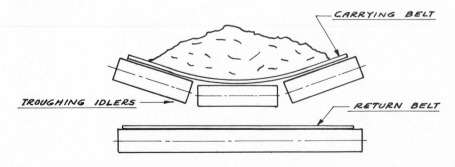

Fig. 3–6. Section through troughed belt conveyor.

The belt is usually troughed construction (see Fig. 3-6) to contain the material. It must be flexible to conform readily to the troughing idlers and also to enable it to negotiate the end pulleys without undue damage. Some belts are constructed with tension members fabricated in the belt to increase its breaking strength, so that comparatively thin belts can be used on long heavy-duty conveyors.

Fig. 3–7. Inclined belt conveyor handling bulk material. (Courtesy Rex Chainbelt Inc.)

Belt conveyors can negotiate reasonable inclines and declines without losing control of material flow. Many installations, using several conveyors in sequence, carry material long distances from mines, quarries, or other sources to processing plants or shipping points.

Buckets are sometimes attached to the belting and the conveyor is arranged to carry the material vertically. The conveyor then is known as a "bucket elevator."

CHAIN CONVEYORS

Many types of conveyors, employing strands of endless chain as the propelling medium, are used to handle bulk material. One kind uses chain with buckets attached; when used to convey the material vertically, it is another form of bucket elevator.

In other arrangements the buckets are mounted on pivots, and the conveyor then can travel both horizontally and vertically. The pivoted buckets remain in a horizontal position until they reach a discharge point where they are tripped, and the buckets then tip or turn over to dump or discharge their contents.

Other chain conveyors have aprons or pans fastened to the strands of endless chains. In the apron conveyor, plates or shapes are overlapping and form a continuous conveying bed. The pan conveyor is similarly constructed, but vertical sides or extensions are attached to or formed integrally with the plates to constitute a continuous moving pan. Both the apron and pan conveyor are flexible and can be arranged to negotiate horizontal and inclined planes.

DRAG, FLIGHT, AND EN-MASSE CONVEYORS

Drag conveyors consist of one or more strands of chain arranged to travel in a fixed path in a trough. Material is then moved or dragged along in the trough. It is suitable for almost any materials excepting those that are free-flowing or have a tendency to pack. Cables can be used in place of chains as the conveying medium for some material. When flights or pushers are attached to the chains or cables, free-flowing material may be conveyed. The conveyor then is known as a flight conveyor.

An en-masse conveyor consists of a stationary casing or conduit with a moving articulated conveying medium fitted with flights. As the flights move through the casing, the material is conveyed and is protected against contamination or spilling from the conveyor. The unit can negotiate horizontal, inclined, and vertical planes. The moving articulated element is usually a chain with the flights formed or cast integrally with the chain links. Cable is used in place of chain at times, and a recent development uses a solid V-belt as the propelling medium.

AERIAL TRAMWAYS AND CABLEWAYS

Aerial tramways are used to convey material long distances. They do not require bridges to cross valleys, rivers, or roadways. The carrier, usually a large bucket or scoop, is suspended from a moving cable. In some other arrangements, the supporting cable is stationary, and a trolley riding on this cable supports the carrier. The carrier then is propelled by another moving traction rope. The carrier can be loaded automatically at one terminal, moved to a discharge point, and then dumped to drop its contents. Points intermediate to the end terminals can thus be served.

An allied unit is the cableway which lifts as well as transports the material. The ability to lift the material distinguishes it from the tramway.

The cableway is used in excavation operations and also in raising concrete into high forms, as when constructing dams. A carriage travels on a cable suspended between towers. The carriage can be raised, conveyed, and then lowered and dumped at any point along the span of the cable.

SCREW CONVEYORS

Screw conveyors are constructed of formed or rolled flights fastened to a shaft, which is usually made of pipe. The flights form a continuous spiral that moves the material along a trough or casing as the shaft turns. The screw conveyor handles dry non-abrasive materials such as seeds, grain, fine coal, etc. Cast screws and housings or casings are desirable if more abrasive material is to be handled.

When damp or sticky material is to be conveyed in a screw conveyor, the flights are mounted outward of the shaft to lessen the probability of material building up on the shaft.

PNEUMATIC SYSTEMS

Pneumatic conveying is accomplished by pressure or by vacuum systems. In the pressure type the material is fed into a pipeline and then propelled by the expanding energy of compressed air. In the vacuum type the reduced pressure or vacuum is applied at the discharge, and the material is moved along the pipeline by atmospheric pressure. In either system means are employed to remove solids from the airstream upon reaching the delivery point. Interlocks are used to introduce materials into the airstream. The vacuum type is probably the best known, since it is frequently used for unloading materials from bulk carriers such as boxcars, ships, barges, etc.

Generally the pneumatic conveyor will handle non-abrasive, dry, small-particle material, pellets, etc. It is ideal for food products and chemicals, since the pipeline gives protection against contamination. Where applicable this conveyor may be more economical than mechanical conveyors, if many changes in direction of flow are encountered, and if multiple delivery points must be served.

Steam-pneumatic conveyors are commonly used to handle ashes from pulverized coal-burning equipment. Here high velocity airflow is produced by a steam exhauster unit and introduced into the pipeline to propel the ash to collector bins or gondola rail cars.

VIBRATING CONVEYORS

Vibrating conveyors are used as feeders from stock bins or silos. The conveyor consists of a trough flexibly supported and vibrated by either a balanced electric power plant or mechanically through centrifugal force generated by rotating unbalanced weights. Any granular non-sticky material can be handled. Excellent volumetric control is provided by the vibrating conveyor, and this is why it is so often used as a feeder.

RELATED EQUIPMENT

There are many other pieces of equipment that are either accessories to the bulk material conveyors mentioned or are independent units that are worthy of description. The tripper (see Fig. 3–8) is used with belt conveyors to permit discharge of material intermediate to the end pulleys. It usually consists of two pulleys with one used to elevate the belting so

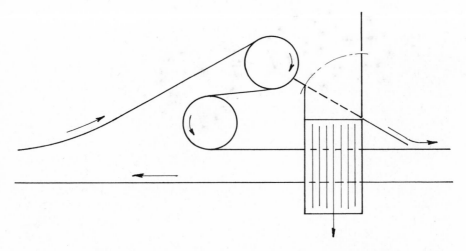

Fig. 3–8. Schematic arrangement of tripper on belt conveyor.

that the material can discharge over it and then by means of a chute or slide be diverted to either side of the conveyor. The pulleys and chute can be mounted on a movable carriage so that multiple discharge points can be served. The chute on the tripper can be provided with a bypass so that material may be directed straight ahead onto the belt for delivery to another tripper or for discharge over the end pulley.

Screens are used to separate the material by size. They can be fixed but sloped to keep the material flowing. Some are of the drum type set at a slight angle. The drum is rotated to keep the material flowing. Other types vibrate or reciprocate to advance the material while it is being sized.

Washers are used to clean the material of debris. Shake-outs are generally used in foundries to clean castings of molding sand. Weighing devices or scales are installed at the loading end of belt conveyors where the belt tension is minimal. When other types of conveyors are used in conjunction with weighing material en route, the conveyor unit is usually mounted on the scale platform. Portable throwers are small belt units used in making storage piles, loading box cars, and trimming the holds of ships. Feeders, in addition to the vibrating type mentioned before, can be short belt, apron, pan, slat, and almost any type of conveyor.

Fig. 3–9. Tripper on belt conveyor; discharge door closed. (Courtesy Rex Chainbelt Inc.)

Many specially designed conveyors and accessories are made to suit the requirements of a specific industry or to meet needs of processing operations. Some examples are the conveyors and machines built for use in mines, for sewage treatment plants, for construction work such as grading, road building, and all forms of heavy construction.

There is no exact or scientific method of determining the best type of conveyor to use for a specific operation. Material-handling engineering is still an art; until it is reduced to a science, it is necessary to rely on experience and some experimentation.

4

Conveyor Applications

An efficient, well-organized operation is not always the one that uses fully automated handling equipment. The degree of automation naturally is dictated by the need. There are many instances where it is unsound to reject a proposed system simply because its first cost cannot be justified by tangible savings. There are also cases where rearrangement of machines or operations can eliminate the need for extensive handling equipment. In other situations, mechanical aids other than cranes, trucks, or conveyors will solve the problem. An illustration of the latter case is the operator whose manufacturing floor was located considerably above the level of his receiving dock where raw material was unloaded. The first consideration was a system combining trucks with horizontal and vertical conveyors. The solution was to install an elevator that raised the incoming freight car to the manufacturing floor level where it was unloaded by simply handling equipment.

The following brief descriptions of conveying systems will illustrate how handling equipment solved some problems. If the examples do not fit the requirements of a condition exactly, they may generate some ideas that will fit.

Assembly Lines

A level roller or wheel conveyor is often used as an assembly line. As parts are added to the assembly, the unit is manually advanced to the next operation. Frequently a roller conveyor is located at floor level and the framework or base of the unit, which may be on a pallet (often the bottom of the shipping crate), is placed on the conveyor. Parts are added as it is advanced, at the will of the line supervisor. This type of assembly line is needed where art is required to make the finished piece; it therefore does not lend itself to a powered line.

When it is necessary to pace the assembly through its various stages, powered conveyor lines are used. The belt conveyor lends itself ideally to this operation since it will function smoothly at slow speeds that can be varied readily to meet the requirements of different units being assembled. Generally the belt conveyor is used for comparatively lightweight items.

Live roll conveyors are also applicable to assembly-line operation. The chief advantage of this conveyor is the ability to stop the forward motion of the work, with very little effort, if it is necessary to perform an operation while the assembly is halted momentarily.

Some assembly lines employ conveyors for the product and another conveyor for the operator so that he can keep pace with the movement of the work. Thus he can, in effect, perform his operation as though he was working at a bench. In the ceramic industry the placing of unfired ware into a sagger is a manual operation. The saggers advance on a belt conveyor while the operator stands on another belt conveyor synchronized with the sagger belt. A third conveyor in back of the operator keeps a supply of unfired ware moving with him. This type of system is usually arranged so that two assembly lines (two sets of three conveyors) form a closed loop. In this way the operator is again performing work while being returned to the starting point.

Chain conveyors make ideal assembly lines and are frequently used in the aircraft and automotive industries. In the majority of these installations other conveyors are arranged to bring a continuous supply of the various parts needed to the proper stations along the assembly route. The work is programmed so that the proper color and style of parts reach an assembly station in the proper sequence to match the model being assembled. In some cases, especially in aircraft work, the forward motion of the line is barely perceptible, and in fact it is on occasion halted for predetermined periods to allow major operations to be performed.

An assembly line may consist of a single conveyor making several turns and even changes in elevation; or it may consist of a series of separate conveyor units. One washing machine line is constructed of two parallel lines of roller conveyors with an endless single strand of chain, equipped with pushers, operating between the two roller conveyors. The machine base is fastened to a pallet which is the bottom of the shipping container. The pallets are advanced on the roller conveyor by the pushers, through various stations where the tub, agitator, drive, etc., are added. At one point water enters the tub and the machine is tested while moving. It passes through a sound-proof room for final testing. As the machines continue, those that need reworking and those that are rejected completely are shunted off the line while approved units continue through a final packing operation. The line makes several passes through the assembly, inspection, and shipping areas. The single strand of chain pushes the washer around curves in the roller conveyor.

Overhead trolley conveyors make ideal assembly lines for many operations. Cars or carriers, suspended from the conveyor line, hold the unit being assembled. With this type of conveyor it is possible to convey the load up over aisles and back down again to a working level after crossing the aisle. Also, with the "power-and-free" feature on this conveyor it is possible to shunt partially completed assemblies into areas for temporary storage or for special operations that cannot be performed on the moving line.

Many other types of conveyors, such as slat, sliding chain, cross-bar, etc., can be used for assembling operations where control over the flow of material must be maintained and all manual transfers from assembly station to station can be eliminated.

Systems

CASE 1

In one plant it was desired to double production, which meant using twice as many machines in one manufacturing area. The plant was located in a large city in an ideal labor market, but there was insufficient space to increase the size of the plant the required amount. The solution was to install belt conveyors over the machines and eliminate the large aisles formerly used to truck material. The belt conveyors served the machines with raw material and carried the finished product to an inspection station. Vertical conveyors then elevated the product to upper floors for further processing and packing. The packed material was then lowered by other conveyors to the shipping dock.

In this plant the processing of the raw material, required before the material could be used in the manufacturing machines, used bulky equipment that was installed on the lower floors for economy. This processing required that raw material in large wooden containers be treated for days in a moist and hot atmosphere. The additional containers that had to be processed to meet the increase in capacity could not be piled into the conditioning room because the "crowding" would interfere with needed air movement. The capacity of the room was doubled by installing a mezzanine floor consisting of level roller conveyor lines with catwalks between. The open construction of the roller conveyor "floor" permitted free airflow.

CASE 2

A manufacturer packed various grades of a product into bags and cartons. When packed, the bags or cartons were palletized and then warehoused. A battery of packing machines delivered their production to a series of automatic pallet loaders. Each loader had the capacity to receive the production from several packing machines.

As the completed pallet loads left the loaders, they were received by a collector conveyor that in turn diverted them through a series of turntables, transfers, and conveyors to vertical conveyor units. Each vertical lowered its pallet loads to the desired floor of the warehouse where industrial lift trucks picked up the load and spotted it in its proper place.

The entire operation beginning at the packing machine and ending in the warehouse local area was automatically controlled. The operations were programmed before each run. The production from a given packing machine was accumulated on a conveyor until a full pallet load had been assembled. The assigned loader then removed the correct number of items from the accumulator conveyor. As the load was discharged from the pallet loader and entered the collector conveyor, a memory device took over and guided it through the system of conveyors and turntables to the vertical conveyor serving the area of the warehouse where that particular load was to be stored.

Complete automation in this case was justified by the high production rate, the variety and types of packaging used, and the expanse of the warehouse.

CASE 3

A manufacturer packaged his product in bags that were to be palletized. The bags were awkward to handle and labor turnover was very high. The production in terms of number of bags per day was extremely low and the operation normally would not have been considered a good prospect for mechanical handling equipment. A handling unit was purchased, however, and the user reported that he expected to pay for it in savings realized in eliminating the turnover of labor.

CASE 4

A large plant where material was mined, processed, and then bagged solved its handling problem by combining bulk conveyors, package conveyors, and industrial lift trucks. A system of troughed belt conveyors carries the large lumps of material to crushers and grinders. Bucket elevators then lift the processed material to a system of belts that delivers it to a group of storage silos. Vibrating feeders under the silos discharge to conveyors that carry the material to the bagging machines in a uniform flow.

Conveyors from the bagging machines deliver the bagged material to pallet loading equipment. Other conveyors handle the pallet loads to storage areas where lift trucks take over to spot the pallets in storage or take them directly to cars or trucks at the shipping dock.

CASE 5

A ready-mix concrete plant found it difficult to control satisfactorily the contents of the various mixes that were specified by customers. A system of conveyors with scales and other measuring devices controls the amount of cement, sand, and gravel. In addition to these ingredients it is necessary to vary the moisture content of the mix depending on the distance that it must be trucked before it is poured. The data showing the exact amount of each ingredient are fed to control equipment that in turn regulates the amount of each material flowing into the truck.

Warehouses

CASE 1

In one warehouse a small number of items accounted for a high percentage of the volume moved. Many shipments consisted of full pallet loads. The popular items were stored adjacent to the shipping dock and so required very little movement of the lift trucks. A few pieces of roller conveyor with lift trucks and four-wheel hand trucks were all the handling equipment needed in this efficient operation.

CASE 2

A warehouse stored a large number of items, and the fast moving items were so numerous that they could not be stored in a small area. Also, the shipping orders rarely included sufficient pieces of an item to permit full pallet load movement.

Four-wheel trucks were used by the pickers to collect an order. When an order was completed or a truck was filled, the truck was moved to a tow conveyor that served the entire picking area. The tow conveyor moved the trucks to the shipping dock while the picker was free to pick another order.

CASE 3

The volume of this plant was sufficient to warrant the installation of automatic picking equipment. A series of punched cards was assembled to correspond to the number of pieces of each item on an order. These cards were first processed on a machine that produced the shipping bill, the invoice, inventory control ticket, etc.

The cards were then automatically rearranged so that they were in accord with the sequence of items in gravity storage racks. Another machine read the cards for the quantity of each item needed, and it sent impulses to controls that operated release mechanisms at the end of each lane in the rack.

A system of collecting conveyors received the items as they exited from the lanes and assembled them in a group in an order-marshaling area.

The controls in this warehouse were operated by punched cards, but punched tape or magnetic tape can be used.

CASE 4

In this warehouse it was felt that the volume did not justify the use of punched cards. It was desired, however, to use automatic picking of orders.

A push-button console was installed. The order forms were printed to agree with the sequence in which items were stored in the gravity storage rack. The console operator then punched the proper code and quantity buttons, and the release mechanism ejected the loads from the rack.

In this case as well as in the warehouse described in Case 3, the loads were released from the rack lanes in sequence to avoid interference on the collecting conveyors. Another available control assigns an area on the collecting conveyor for each item to be picked. As the assigned area or spot on the conveyor arrives at the proper lane, an item is released. In this way the entire surface of the collecting conveyor is utilized, and the gaps or voids on the collecting conveyors, as occur with sequential systems, are eliminated. This is a desirable feature on high-volume operations as it permits the collecting conveyor to run at a slower speed and contributes to better handling.

CASE 5

To avoid the travel of picking men, this warehouse used lanes of conveyors to bring the pallet load to a picking aisle. The pickers then removed items from the pallets and placed them onto a conveyor that traveled to an order-marshaling area. Each picker operated in a comparatively small area of the aisle.

NEED FOR IMPROVED LOADING SYSTEMS

Among the many modifications possible to reduce the handling time in warehouse operations are the following:

1. Items received loose can be palletized on an automatic pallet loader.
2. Pallet loads received in the warehouse can be depalletized on a pallet unloader so that the individual pieces can be placed into gravity storage racks.

3. Pickers can be furnished with powered trucks to speed their movement from rack to rack.

Most of the present-day automatic installations in warehouses have concentrated on automatic picking. The loading of the racks remains a manual operation. In some cases, where the physical dimensions of the items do not vary too greatly, conveyors can be utilized to carry the item to the proper level and then divert it into its designated lane.

Another expensive manual function is in loading over-the-road trucks at the shipping platform. The trailer can be spotted at the dock, and the tractor then released for other work. Many types of conveyors are available to carry the items into the trailer, but the stacking of the individual pieces is a manual operation representing about two manhours of work per trailer. In some plants, containers are loaded with orders in the warehouse prior to truck arrival. When the truck does reach the dock, it is necessary only to wheel in, or truck in, the containers. This system reduces the truck loading time, but these savings are offset somewhat by the labor required to load the containers. Also, all containers are not completely filled, and this represents some loss in tonnage that the truck transports.

The important point here is that while technology has produced good high-speed picking operations, there is ample opportunity to: (1) develop suitable systems to load the racks for all loads, and (2) develop a method of speeding the loading of tractor-trailers after the goods reach the shipping platform.

5

Gravity Conveyors

Gravity conveyors include chutes or slides, roller conveyors, and wheel conveyors, in straight sections, curves, and spirals.

Chutes

STRAIGHT CHUTES

The most common straight chute has a solid bottom bed with retaining sides or guards. Figure 5–1 shows cross-sections of the designs most often used. The tops of the side guards can be reinforced by beading the metal

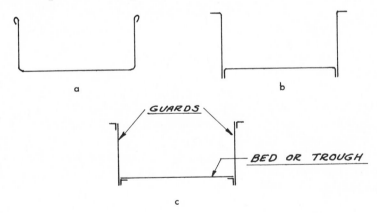

Fig. 5–1. Typical chute constructions. (a) Unit. (b) Three-piece. (c) Structural.

as shown in the unit construction, by formed flanges as shown in the three-piece construction, or by angle members. (The type of reinforcement used is not limited to the design on which it is illustrated.)

Chutes are used to lower cartons, boxes, or bagged material, and they are normally constructed of hot rolled or galvanized sheet metal. Smooth metals such as lustre finish cold rolled steel, stainless steel, etc., are seldom required. The smooth surface of such metals has a tendency to create a vacuum under the package and retard its movement.

If the contents of the packages tend to escape the containers, resulting leakage will collect in corners, joints, etc., and if the material is vulnerable to moisture, erosion will result. Also, some material will build up in the chute and retard travel.

Since gravity is the motive force in a chute, there is very little control over speed, and the package will accelerate noticeably on long chutes. The angle of decline is such that the lightest package can slide; heavier packages will slide into and damage the lighter loads. Under these conditions chutes are not suitable for fragile loads.

When constructed of galvanized metal, the chute should be installed at an angle of about 20°. If made of hot rolled metal, the angle should be 25°; if smooth metal is used, the angle should be increased to 30° or more. These grades are based on operation in a reasonably dry atmosphere such as a heated area. If the humidity is normally high, the grades will have to be increased about 25 per cent. If humidity fluctuates between high and low, the action in the chute will be erratic.

The use of straight chutes should be confined to short runs—up to approximately fifteen feet in length. The chief use for the straight chute is as an economical transfer between conveyors installed at different elevations. When such transfers are short and loads are spaced, fragile packages can be conveyed if provisions are made to stop the feeding conveyor when the discharge of the chute is blocked.

Chutes are frequently used at the end of conveyor lines to bring the package down to a working elevation. In this arrangement fragile loads will be damaged if they are permitted to accumulate in the chute.

At times the chute is required to change direction, and a curve is then inserted as shown in Fig. 5–2. The sliding angle on the outer edge of the curve is the same as the angle in the straight portions of the chute. The angle at the inside of the curve is steep, and the slope increases as the inside radius R decreases.

The front inside corner of a rigid load, such as a carton or box, tips as it enters the curved portion, and this corner meets the lesser angle of the lower straight portion as it leaves the curve. This action may be damaging to some loads, but more important is the fact that the tipping of the load increases the need for more space between the side guards. Therefore, a chute that includes a curve will have to be wider than a straight chute for the same package. Means of calculating the width required will be covered later in the discussion of spiral chutes.

The larger the radius R, the smoother the transition between the slope on the straight portions and the inside of the curve. Limitations of space, however, usually require that the radius be kept small. The minimum radius should be one quarter of width W. The recommended radius is about one half of W.

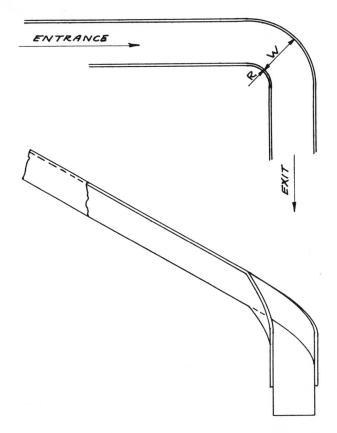

Fig. 5–2. Chute with intermediate curved section.

SPIRAL CHUTES

Spiral chutes are helical in form, but accepted nomenclature lists all of the conveyors built in this manner as spirals. They consist of one or more 360° turns.

There are several forms of beds or troughs, as shown in Fig. 5–3. The flat bed is used most often because it is the most economical to manufacture. In Fig. 5–3 both the flat bed and the concave bed are shown built around a core or supporting column. The banked bed is shown as "open" construction. Any form of bed can be used with either core or open design. The illustration shows angles used to connect the bed to the core and the guards to the bed. Some manufacturers use flanged bed plates and thus eliminate the angles. Also, any form of reinforcement may be used at the top of the guard, for example, those shown in Fig. 5–1 for straight chutes.

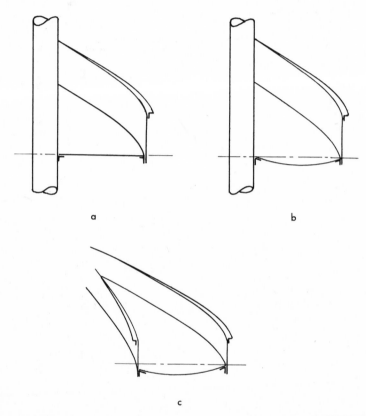

a   b

c

Fig. 5–3. Typical spiral chute construction. (a) Flat bed. (b) Concave bed. (c) Banked bed.

Some cores are constructed of pipe; others are formed of rolled metal. In the core-type spiral, the inside radius is small, and thus results in a considerable difference in angle of decline between the outer and inner edges of the bed.

In the open construction the inside radius can be large and the difference in the slopes is less, resulting in less tipping of the load as it descends the spiral. The open-type spiral is needed when the chute is installed around a building column.

Spiral chutes have more control over the speed of travel of varying weight loads than do straight chutes. As the weight of the load increases and therefore travels faster, its centrifugal force increases the pressure against the outer guard. This increased friction tends to reduce the speed of the heavier loads. The practical value of this feature is lessened somewhat on rigid loads such as cartons and boxes, especially in the flat bed core construction. The tipping of the load presents only a corner or edge to the guard and little retarding friction results.

The concave bed construction invites the small light loads to ride in the "valley" of the bed. These loads then travel a lesser distance and on a greater slope than do the larger loads that tend to fill the trough. Also,

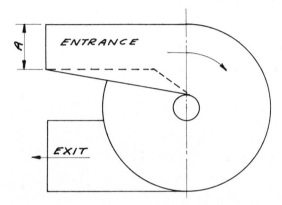

Fig. 5–4. Entrance and exits for spiral chute.

small heavy loads that are forced toward the outer edge by centrifugal action have to "climb" the rise in the bed. The concave bed, then, has greater control over the speed of varying weight loads. The banked bed improves this control over speed and is the most effective of the designs.

With the core construction, the desirable ratio of inside radius to width of trough given for curves in straight chutes cannot be maintained. The spiral normally, however, has only one entrance and one exit, and these transitions from straight chute to curved chute can be given special treatment. The width of the trough or bed in the spiral is more than the width needed in the straight chute leading to the spiral. This permits an arrangement as shown in Fig. 5–4. All loads are forced to enter the spiral at the outer edge where the sliding angles are the same. The opening A in the straight chute should be as small as possible. This narrow width can be extended, as shown by dotted lines, to near the spiral entrance, where it must be increased to allow clearance for the load as it enters the curve.

The exit chute should be constructed with parallel sides as shown. Most descending loads will travel against the outer guard of the spiral where the angle of decline is the same as the angle of the straight exit chute. There are some packages that may ride toward the inside of the spiral, and these will meet an abrupt change in angle of slope as they enter the straight chute. There is no practical way to correct this condition economically. The parallel side construction, rather than the tapered construction shown for the entrance chute, prevents the loads from wedging as they slide down the chute. Many packages will be askew as they exit from the spiral.

The segments that form the bed of the spiral chute are almost always formed on dies. The resulting standard widths are shown in Table 5–1 with the recommended maximum size package that can be conveyed.

Table 5–1. Standard spiral chute trough widths and capacities.

Trough Width	Maximum Package Size		
	Length	Width	Height
12"	15"	9"	6"
18"	20"	12"	10"
24"	30"	18"	16"
30"	36"	22"	20"
36"	48"	26"	24"
42"	52"	30"	28"
48"	60"	36"	30"

This table should be used only as a guide, because manufacturers vary the diameter of the cores they use and the exact capacity of the different spirals will change slightly. Also, if an open construction is used, the package size capacity will increase as the inside radius is enlarged.

It is possible to approximate the required width of trough needed for a given package by careful interpolation. After arriving at a probable standard width, a more exact check, while not mathematically perfect, can be made with the method shown in Fig. 5–5. If it is felt that a special width may be necessary, it would be well to consider another more economical method of handling the load, such as a declined belt conveyor.

It is not necessary to design the spiral with an exact 20°, 25°, etc., slope at the outer edge. The pitch (drop in 360°) may have to be adjusted to accommodate available vertical space. It should be to the nearest 6", i.e., 12'–0", 12'–6", 13'–0", etc. Additional adjustment in the vertical drop of the entrance and exit chutes is permissible.

As cartons or similar rigid loads cannot lie flat in the spiral, humid atmospheric conditions do not affect movement. Therefore, for these rigid loads the angle of decline is not affected as it is in straight chutes. If semifluid loads like bagged material are handled, however, humidity does affect the speed, and spirals are treated in the same manner as are

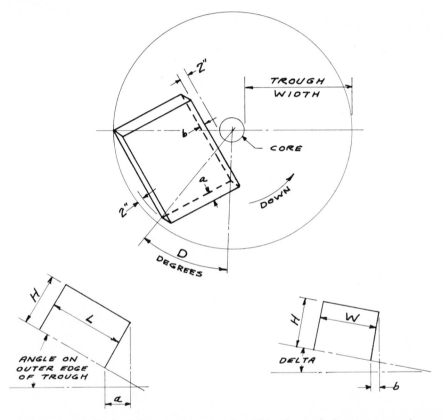

Fig. 5–5. Method of determining trough width of spiral chute. L = package length in inches; W = package width in inches; H = package height in inches; P = spiral pitch in inches; sine angle $\delta = \dfrac{P \times D}{360 \times W}$.

straight chutes. If cartons or bags are *wet*, they will not slide unless the angle is increased an impractical amount. They will require manual assistance at times.

Rarely is it economical to construct the spiral of smooth metals such as lustre finish cold rolled steel or stainless steel. If these metals are used in a spiral, there is no need to increase the pitch when handling rigid loads as they cannot lie flat and create a vacuum.

Roller Conveyors

The rollers on standard conveyors vary from $\frac{3}{4}''$ diameter to $3\frac{1}{2}''$ diameter. The load-carrying capacity ratings vary from 20# to 2,500# per roller. The majority of conveyor systems use rollers from $1\frac{1}{2}''$ to $2\frac{1}{2}''$ diameter, and these are rated at 70# to 750# capacity per roller.

To assure smooth movement of loads over the conveyor, there should be a minimum of three rollers under a load at all times. When the load has a rigid riding surface, as is the case with metal or wood pallets, boxes, and firm cartons, the minimum of three rollers will be satisfactory. Some cartons, however, are constructed of comparatively soft stock, and it may be necessary to close the spacing of the rollers to insure movement at minimum grades. Semifluid loads like bundles or bags can be conveyed on roller conveyors, but the rollers have to be closely spaced to prevent the package from sagging into the spaces between the rollers. Roller spacing will be discussed in greater detail when the subject of grades is covered. Standard roller spacing most often used is 3", 4", or 6".

The bearings used in standard conveyors consist of a full complement of balls operating in unground races. Caged ball bearings or roller bearings in ground races are not required in the normal application. The rollers are rarely loaded to their rated capacity in conveyor systems.

Figure 5–6 shows cross-sections through the two roller conveyors most often used. The frames can be structural angles or channels, or formed channel shapes. Auxiliary guardrails, when required, are usually structural or formed angles, and these are most often used on the sections with

a   b

Fig. 5–6. Section through roller conveyor. (a) Rollers in low position. (b) Rollers in high position.

rollers in high position. High sheet-metal guards may be needed for some installations. When rollers are set high in the frame, guards may not be required on straight sections but probably will be needed on the outside of curved sections.

Rollers are constructed of steel tubing with a bearing mounted in each end of the tube. The outer races of the bearings rotate with the tube, while the inner races are locked to a stationary shaft which in turn is locked in the frame structure. Figure 5–7 shows two assemblies that are popular. On one assembly, the rounded end of the tube is shown as turned in to receive the bearing. Other methods of rounding the tube are available and equally effective.

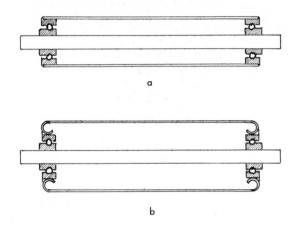

Fig. 5–7. Roller construction. (a) Straight roller. (b) Round-end roller.

The larger the ratio between the roller diameter and the bearing diameter, the livelier the roller. The friction of the bearings used in standard roller conveyors will vary slightly, but a figure of 2 per cent will prove adequate for all practical purposes. When bearings are grease-packed or seals are used for any other purpose, the friction will be nearer 5 per cent.

Curved sections of roller conveyors match the construction of the straight sections. The width of the conveyor is usually determined by the clearance required for a package to negotiate the curve. Figure 5–8 gives the formula for calculating the distance needed between frames for rollers in low position and between guards if they are used. The inside radius of standard curved sections is from 30″ to 36″, depending on the manufacturer.

The standard widths of roller conveyors are 6″, 10″ 12″, 14″, 16″, 18″, 20″, 24″, 30″, 36″, 42″, and 48″. In most cases the "width" refers to nominal roller length. The actual length of the roller may vary, but the distance between frames is considered to be nominal roller plus one inch with most manufacturers. If only large uniform-sized loads are handled, it is possible to use a comparatively narrow conveyor with rollers in high position and auxiliary guards to contain the packages.

The rollers used in curved sections may be the following: the single roller used in straight sections, a series of two or more rollers arranged

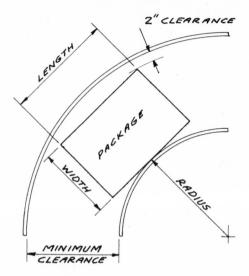

Fig. 5–8. Formula for clearance required in roller curve:

$$\text{Min. clearance} = \sqrt{(\text{Radius} + \text{Width})^2 + \left(\frac{\text{Length}}{2}\right)^2} - \text{Radius} + 2''.$$

differentially, or tapered rollers. Figure 5–9 shows the three arrangements available. The straight roller construction will prove satisfactory where it is not damaging for packages to rub the outside frame or the guard. Most packages will skew as they negotiate this type of curve.

The differential construction is recommended where there is a wide range in package sizes, because the outer and inner rollers can revolve at different speeds. The need for the packages to slide on the rollers as they travel around the curve is reduced, and therefore the tendency to skew is lessened.

Curves that are equipped with tapered rollers assure that the package will hold its position as it negotiates the curve. It is possible to eliminate outer guards, although safety measures may require a guard if the conveyor is installed overhead or if heavier loads may become dislodged on lines nearer to the floor level. Another advantage of this construction is that less grade is required in the curve to assure package travel.

Many installations of level roller conveyors are made to aid in manually advancing the load. When so used, the spacing of rollers can be the maximum permitted with three rollers under the shortest package or load. If the item being moved is unevenly loaded, it may be necessary to use closer spacing to prevent the unit from tipping. As the friction for free-running bearings is only 2 per cent, it is possible to advance heavy loads with very little manual effort.

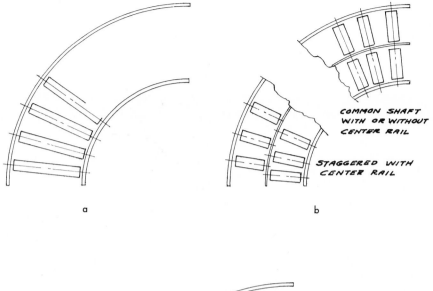

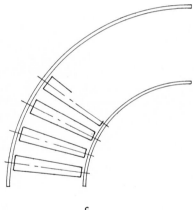

Fig. 5–9. Typical roller conveyor curves. (a) Straight rollers. (b) Differential rollers. (c) Tapered rollers.

The majority of installations employ the force of gravity to advance the load, and the proper grade or drop per linear unit is difficult to arrive at in a scientific manner. Among the many conditions that must be considered are:

1. Type of bearing in the roller—free-running or grease-packed.
2. Condition of the bottom of the package or commodity being conveyed—steel, wood, hard carton stock, or soft material.
3. Atmospheric conditions—dry, humid, clean, dusty, etc.

4. Operating requirements—whether packages flow continuously or are caused to stop on the conveyor; if the latter, whether they are held for long periods before being released.

Each of these conditions is worthy of separate discussion.

Bearings. In most cases the free-running bearing is used. Only a small amount of lubricant may be present in the bearing; usually it is the coating that the bearing parts normally receive in the manufacturing process. The friction of this bearing is then not affected by temperature fluctu-

Fig. 5–10. Roller conveyors at carton-packing stations. (Courtesy Lamson Corporation.)

ations. All figures that will be given for recommended grades are based on free-running bearings. Grease-packed and/or sealed bearings are normally used only where severe corrosive or dusty conditions exist. The lines usually are not long and often auxiliary power equipment is employed to advance the loads.

Load Riding Surface. The bottom or riding surface of the load is the most important consideration. If the load has a firm metal or wood base, it probably will not be deformed over the rollers due to its weight. In this case there is practically no resistance to movement as it rolls over the conveyor. If the bottom is soft wood or a carton, the comparatively soft bottom will tend to conform to the shape of the rollers, and the package will undulate as it moves over the conveyor. The effort needed to raise the load slightly over the rollers then requires increased grade to keep it moving. Ordinary firm carton stock becomes very soft if subjected to moisture.

Any strapping or wire binding on the package will likewise affect its free movement on roller conveyors. If flat strapping is pulled tight, it probably will have little effect unless the act of applying the strapping

Fig. 5–11. Roller conveyor aiding manual advancement of flasks in a foundry. (Courtesy Alvey-Ferguson Company.)

has bulged the package so that it is no longer flat. Round wire binding almost always retards free flow, and often it is necessary to handle this kind of package on a power conveyor.

Atmospheric Conditions. If the air surrounding the conveyor is humid, a soft wood bottom or an ordinary carton will conform to the rollers even when the contents of the package are comparatively lightweight. A system of conveyors installed in an inland dry area may operate at one half to two thirds the grade required of an identical system installed in a seacoast area.

If the surrounding area is dusty and it is desired to use free-running bearings, it may be necessary to specify "dry" bearings that have been cleared of all oil. This is especially true if abrasive or corrosive-type dusts are present.

Operating Conditions. When the roller conveyor is only a transportation line, and loads move continuously and frequently enough to keep the rollers turning, only a minimum grade is needed. Under such normal conditions, an infrequent stoppage may require a group of loads to accumulate before the line will again start flowing in a free manner.

When the packages are stopped on the conveyor at frequent intervals and remain stopped for periods of, say, a half to one hour (start-stop operation), the packages settle down between the rollers. The grade will then have to be greater than for a simple transportation line.

If the conveyor is used for storage over long periods, as in a warehouse, the grades may have to be double the amount normally used for transportation lines.

DETERMINING GRADE

As can be readily seen from the preceding paragraphs, it is impossible to specify a grade that would be suitable for all conditions. It is possible, however, to use the grades given in Table 5–2 as guides. These grades will prove satisfactory where there is a realization that, because the motive force is gravity, an occasional temporary blockade or an occasional runaway may occur. At times some manual assistance may even be necessary.

If it is felt that more accurate grade data are required, it can be obtained by a series of tests in the plant with the actual commodity to be conveyed. If accurate control over the rate of flow is needed, a powered conveyor system rather than a gravity conveyor system should be used.

The grades in Table 5–2 are based on rollers having an outside diameter about 2.5 times the diameter of the ball circle in the bearing. This ratio will vary somewhat with different manufacturers. If the ratio is less than 2 to 1, the grades shown must be increased.

It is important to keep the grade or drop in the system at a minimum. The available vertical height is usually limited; if the height is wasted by excessive grades, it will be necessary to use a greater number of power conveyors or "grade retrievers." Excessive grades also are objectionable, because they permit the packages to accelerate excessively. Heavy loads, for instance, over 100#, should not be handled on excessively long lines. Extremely heavy loads should not be handled on the same conveyors designed to convey light loads.

It is possible to use grades less than those shown in the table by using rollers on close centers when conveying soft loads. The closer spacing prevents the load from sagging excessively. Since the spacing is closed, however, the number of rollers under a package increases, and this greater mass must be accelerated when the package starts from rest.

It will be noted that the grade or drop in a 90° curve is slight, and, because the inside radius is comparatively large, there is little difference in the angle of slope between the outside and inside of the curve. Therefore there is little tipping of the package as it negotiates the turns.

Table 5–2. Grades for roller conveyors.

| | | Grade or Drop in Inches | | | | | |
| | | Per Foot | | | Per 90° Curve* | | |
	Type of Load	Convey Only	Start Stop	Storage	Straight Roll	Diff. Roll	Taper Roll
Dry Areas	Metal Pans Wood Boxes	0.30	0.30	0.30	3	3	2
	Cartons to 70#	0.40	0.50	0.70	4	4	3
	Cartons over 70#	0.50	0.65	0.90	5	4	3
Humid Areas	Metal Pans Wood Boxes	0.30	0.30	0.30	3	3	2
	Cartons to 70#	0.50	0.60	0.90	5	4	3
	Cartons over 70#	0.60	0.70	1.00	6	5	4

*Proportion drop for other than 90°.

When a series of curves are assembled to form a spiral, the drop per curve is increased considerably. This is to provide clearance for the package height. The roller conveyor with its horizontal supporting structure will be about 6″ deep, and this must be added to package clearance to determine the minimum pitch per 360° turn. Assume a package 24″ high and allow 2″ for clearance. This 26″ when added to the conveyor depth gives a minimum pitch of 32″ or 8″ per 90° turn.

In most spirals the grade per curve will exceed the drop shown in Table 5–2. The movement of packages will be fast, and high sheet-metal guards are often required to control the flow of the package in the spiral. The effectiveness of differential and tapered rollers is lost to some extent when rigid packages are handled. Comparatively soft loads will tend to conform to the warp in the curves and some control over skewing results.

A spiral should never be used for storage when miscellaneous size loads are being handled. The smaller packages could be crushed or become wedged. The magnitude of the pressure developed in a spiral of many turns can be enough to damage even rugged packages and their contents.

Fig. 5–12. Roller gravity spirals. (Courtesy Lamson Corporation.)

Measurable pressures will develop even on long straight lines set at minimum grades. On the straight conveyor, however, the packages bear flat one against the other, and the pressure is distributed over the entire end area of the package. The pressure developed by an accumulation of packages can be readily calculated. If the conveyor is graded at ½″ per foot, the force, parallel to the conveyor, will be about 4# for each 100# of live load. The friction of 2 per cent will reduce this pressure to about 2# for each 100# of load.

STOPS

Start-stop belt conveyors make effective stop mechanisms. When arranged properly, the pressure is distributed over the area of the package. More economical stops are those employing plates, fingers, or rollers that interrupt the flow of the package. These latter stops, however, concentrate the pressure in a small area of the package and damage may result.

ACCESSORIES

Many accessories are available to permit considerable flexibility in roller conveyor systems. The major units are: switches, gates, spurs, converging and diverging sections, ball transfers, and deflectors. Figure 5–13 illustrates these items.

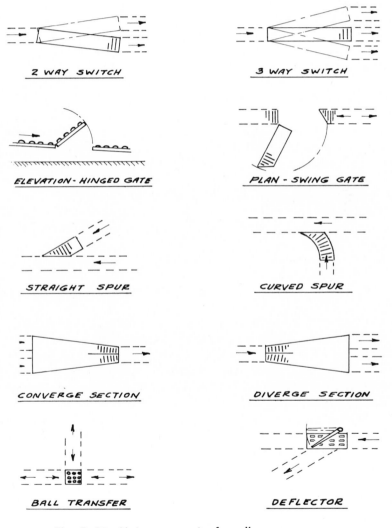

Fig. 5–13. Major accessories for roller conveyors.

The switch is usually a 10'–0" or longer section of roller conveyor that can be manually or mechanically adjusted to permit packages from a single line to be transferred to two or more other lines.

Gate sections are hinged vertically or horizontally to open an aisle in the conveyor line. They may be counterweighted to permit manual operation, or they can be operated by hand or power winches.

Spurs are fixed short sections of straight or curved units to permit transfer of packages between a spur line and a main conveyor line. If used to transfer to the main line as illustrated, provision must be made to prevent the packages from entering from the spur line and interfering with those traveling on the main line. The merging can be automatic, and some form of stop mechanism can be provided in the spur line to allow packages to enter the main line only when traffic permits. The grade in the spur area is increased to allow the package to slide across the rollers in the main line until they have assumed a proper traveling attitude.

The converging and diverging sections are constructed similarly, and usually the packages are manually assisted across the transfer. Automatic operation is possible with reasonably uniform size packages and with packages that have a rigid riding surface. If miscellaneous size loads or soft-bottom loads are being handled, a switch will perform the transfer better.

Ball transfers are units, inserted in the system, consisting of a series of closely spaced ball casters. The transfer is manual and loads can be moved from line to line with little effort. As the casters present only point contacts with the load, these transfers are confined to systems handling rigid-bottom commodities. Soft loads will be depressed by the balls, and it would be difficult to maneuver the loads. In many cases where reasonably lightweight soft loads are being handled, a transfer plate of solid metal will prove to be more practical.

Deflectors require special treatment. Any deflector bar thrown across a standard roller conveyor would offer enough resistance to stop the package before it is completely diverted. Therefore, a series of ball or swivel casters are inserted in the conveyor at the deflector area. Then, when a package is deflected by the bar, it (the package) readily changes its direction and travels by gravity into the receiving line.

To negotiate curves, switches, and other transfers on roller conveyor systems, the item being handled should always be conveyed with its long dimension in the direction of travel. The greater the ratio of length to width, the better the operation will be around curves, etc. Square or nearly square packages will tend to turn on curves and many will jam. Such packages never travel properly over switches, spurs, or deflectors.

When straight sections of roller conveyors are used for storage purposes, the package may travel with its long dimension *across* the conveyor. This is done in some instances to permit more units to be stored in the length of the storage line. It is best in these cases to arrange guardrails (or side frames) so that there is a minimum of package clearance. This prevents the package from skewing and jamming.

SPECIAL CONSTRUCTIONS

There are many modified arrangements of roller conveyors that can be applied to meet special requirements. One such modification is to make guards of sections of roller or wheel conveyors to reduce the friction of the package bearing against the guard.

On packing lines the bed of the conveyor is frequently tilted to make the open top of the package more accessible to the packer. These tilted lines often use another section of conveyor to act as a support as well as a guard.

Three rail frames, mounting two sets of rollers, double the number of supporting members under the load. The capacity of the conveyor is then increased without using a heavier-duty roller. Other three-rail sections have the center rail advanced slightly so that the two sets of rollers present a herringbone arrangement. This retards the motion of a package and effectively brakes the movement. In some cases the center rail is adjustable so that the brake can be applied at the will of an operator.

As mentioned earlier, rollers are made in a wide range of diameters. The small rollers can be placed on very close centers to convey very short loads or semifluid loads such as bagged material. The larger rollers are used for heavy unit loads and where severe shock is encountered. The loading condition may readily determine the type of roller to use rather than static loading due to weight alone.

When heavy loads are handled, the conveyor is usually level or graded slightly to reduce the manual effort needed to advance the load. If the grade is sufficient to allow the load to move by gravity, the conveyor should be very short to avoid excessive acceleration.

Rollers usually are made of steel tubing but for special purposes can be made of hard wood, non-ferrous metals, or plastic tubing. Also, some steel rollers are plated or covered with rubber or plastics.

Wheel Conveyors

A typical cross-section through this conveyor is illustrated in Fig. 5–14. The shafts are spaced on 3″ centers, and alternate shafts have wheels interspaced to distribute them evenly under a package.

Standard widths are 12″, 15″, and 18″, with the number of wheels varying between 8 and 22 per foot of conveyor. The width is measured to the

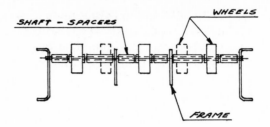

Fig. 5–14. Section through wheel conveyor.

outside of the conveyor frames. Curved sections are available to match the straight section construction.

Frames and/or wheels are available in steel or aluminum. In either case the wheels are very light and offer little resistance to packages starting from rest on graded lines. The grades required are about half those required for roller conveyors.

The light construction of the wheel conveyor limits its use to comparatively lightweight loads. This construction, however, makes the conveyor ideal as a portable unit. Complete lines can readily be assembled in shipping and receiving areas to aid in loading and unloading cars and trucks. The lines can be easily dismantled and stored away when not in use. Sections of wheel conveyors are often carried by trucks to assist loading and unloading operations when away from large docks.

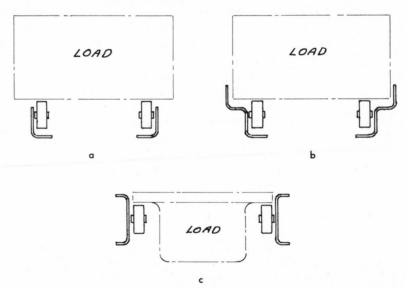

Fig. 5–15. Wheel conveyor skid assemblies. (a) Plain skids. (b) Skids with built-in guards. (c) Wheel skid conveyor.

Wheel conveyors can be used for storage as well as for transportation. When used in storage lines where the commodity may stay at rest for long periods, soft-bottom loads will conform more readily to the wheels than would the same load on a roller conveyor. Therefore the grade required in storage lines, in many cases, will be the same as that needed for a roller conveyor. As the starting friction of the wheel is low, the wheel conveyor is best for storage lines for all light, dry, and reasonably firm packages.

Curved sections make ideal turns for packages because of their differential construction. The packages retain their position very well. When curved units are made into a spiral, however, the grade or drop in the curve must be increased to provide package clearance. When the package is high, requiring drops of 6″ or more per 90° curve, the package may fail to travel. The leading corner of the package can foul against the side of a wheel.

In addition to its lightweight advantage and its need for very little vertical drop to handle loads, the wheel conveyor has another unique feature. Single rails or skids as shown in Fig. 5–15 are available in many forms. The illustration shows one form of one piece supporting frame and guard. Many other arrangements are possible. A pair of these skids can be used in storage racks in place of sections of roller or wheel conveyors. The spread of the pair of skids can be altered to accommodate changes in the size of package stored.

The single rail construction also can be used on conveyor lines to handle items with projections on the bottom as shown in Fig. 5–15.

In the foregoing discussions on roller and wheel conveyors, no mention has been made of supporting structures for the conveyors. Standard supports and hangers are available for both conveyors when installed in a fixed position. Portable supports, including adjustable types, are made for both conveyors.

Also, it is possible to convey any shape of commodity on these conveyors when a sheet of plywood or other simple pallet is used.

One final reminder applies to any type of gravity conveyor. Don't consider these conveyors if: (1) fragile loads are intermixed with heavy loads; (2) complete and accurate control over rate of flow is essential; (3) heavy loads can accelerate beyond control.

6

Belt Conveyors

Practically all belt conveyors designed to handle unit loads are flat-bed construction and so differ in appearance from the usual troughed-bed design that handles bulk material. Figure 6–1 shows two of the most common arrangements. The frames may take many forms: rollers can be in high or low position in any type of wood or metal frame; shelves or work benches may be incorporated on either or both sides of the frame; the slider bed may be wood, metal, or any reasonably smooth material.

The roller spacing in roller-bed construction depends on the length and weight of the load and the type of belting used. All belting tends to sag between the rollers, and heavy items will undulate between rollers spaced too far apart. If this condition exists, the power needed to operate the conveyor will be excessive. It is best to design the conveyor so that two rollers always support loads or packages in excess of 25# in weight.

The standard spacings of rollers are 6", 8", 12", and 15". Closer spacing is available and greater spacings of 24", 30", and even 36" are permissible on conveyors handling very light loads.

If very thin, flexible belting is used, the rollers should be closely spaced. If three- and four-ply or heavier canvas and rubber belting is specified, the roller spacing can be increased to the maximum permitted by the length and weight of the package or load.

When roller-bed conveyors are inclined, the roller spacing must be close enough to assure that the load will travel flat on the belting. If the load is allowed to undulate as it negotiates the incline, it will lose contact with the belting, and slipping will occur. Often the angled portion of a conveyor will have closer roller spacing than does the horizontal portion.

Slider-bed construction assures level, smooth handling on the conveyor and is ideal for all comparatively light loads. A good rule is to limit the use of this design to loads weighing not over 50# per square foot of riding surface. If the load does not have a solid, flat bottom, the loading limit must be checked on the basis of the area in contact with the belting.

The belt conveyor is an ideal medium for raising or lowering packages where it is necessary to keep control over the movement of the load.

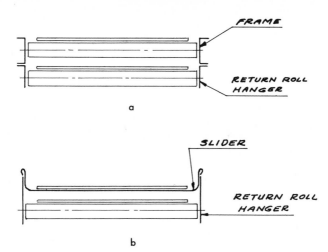

Fig. 6–1. Section through belt conveyors. (a) Roller bed. (b) Slider bed.

Special belting surfaces permit comparatively steep angles. Fragile loads can be handled simultaneously with heavy rugged items.

The roller used in most package conveyors is the same unit used in gravity roller conveyors. Since the belt conveyor runs continuously, the bearings in the rollers are subject to greater wear than they would normally receive in the gravity conveyor. However, the loading rarely equals the rating of the bearing, and the life expectancy will prove satisfactory for all conveyor speeds up to about 200 feet per minute. At speeds over 120 FPM the noise of the free balls in the bearings may become objectionable. The noise level can be reduced by using grease-packed bearings which are available in most of the standard sizes by the addition of seals to the free-running bearing.

The load rating recommended by the manufacturer is normally based on a roller surface speed of 60 FPM and 5,000 hours bearing life. (Bearing life is the number of hours of operation that 90 per cent of the bearings will complete without failure.) The roller load rating can be determined from the following equation, which is based on ASA Standard B 3.11-1959:

$$P = fZ^{2/3}D^{1.8}d^{1/3}$$

in which

P = roller rating in pounds at surface speed of 60 FPM and life of 5,000 hours.
f = factor of 500 which is recommended for the type of bearing used in standard rollers.
Z = number of balls in the bearing.
D = diameter of balls in inches.
d = diameter of roller in inches.

As an aid to using the above formula, Table 6–1 gives the values of Z, D, and d for the sizes usually found in package belt-conveyor construction. If conveyor speed is other than 60 FPM, the load rating can be modified by using the speed factor in Table 6–2. If a life rating of other than 5,000 hours is needed, the rating for the desired life can be found by using the life factor, also given in Table 6–2.

Table 6–1. Factors for calculating load ratings of rollers.

Roller Diameter d	$d^{1/3}$	Ball Diameter D	$D^{1.8}$	Number of Balls Z	$Z^{2/3}$
3/4"	0.908	1/8"	0.024	7	3.66
1"	1.000	5/32"	0.036	8	4.00
1-1/4"	1.077	3/16"	0.049	9	4.33
1-1/2"	1.145	1/4"	0.083	10	4.64
1.9"	1.238	9/32"	0.102	11	4.95
2"	1.260	5/16"	0.123	12	5.24
2-1/4"	1.310	3/8"	0.171	13	5.53
2-1/2"	1.358	7/16"	0.225	14	5.81
2-9/16"	1.368	1/2"	0.288	15	6.08
3"	1.442			16	6.35
3-1/2"	1.518			17	6.61
				18	6.87

Table 6–2. Factor for calculating life of bearings.

Speed		Life	
Desired Speed – FPM	Factor	Desired Life – Hours	Factor
20	1.44	2,000	1.36
40	1.14	3,000	1.19
60	1.00	4,000	1.08
80	0.91	5,000	1.00
100	0.84	6,000	0.94
120	0.79	7,000	0.89
140	0.75	8,000	0.86
160	0.72	9,000	0.82
180	0.69	10,000	0.79
200	0.67		

A more complete analysis of roller and shaft ratings is given in CEMA Standard #401-1962, available from Conveyor Equipment Manufacturers Association, Washington, D. C. 20005.

Belting

The belting is the most expensive single item used to construct a belt conveyor, and also is the most vulnerable to damage if not properly applied. Various types of belting are available; in many instances several kinds will satisfy a particular requirement. In such cases the market price becomes the factor that determines the type to use. The descriptions that are given later will aid the engineer in determining the type best suited to the needs of the conveyor.

SIZE

In general, the size of the belt is determined by the stresses present. (The method of finding the value of these stresses will be covered later.) The package size, however, in many cases will determine the width of belting required. The thickness or number of plies in the belting depends to a great extent on the service required of the conveyor. To illustrate: assume a mixture of loads varying from 10″ to 26″ in width. The widest load indicates that a 30″ conveyor with a distance of 31″ between guards should be used. The belting can be 30″ wide, but a 24″ belt may satisfy requirements. If the service is transportation only, the belting will track reasonably well and the open spaces at each side will be stable at about 3½″. The narrow 10″ package, if its contents are balanced, should negotiate the conveyor even if it rides completely to one side of the conveyor. If, however, the packages are to be deflected from the conveyor along its route, the deflecting packages tend to pull the belting off its center course; the open space on the side can then increase to almost the full 7″ permitted by the 24″ belt in the 31″ bed. The 10″ package would then fall through or jam in this gap. In this installation the decision to use a 24″ or a 30″ belt would depend on package size and service required of the conveyor.

The thickness or number of plies required in the belting for the conveyor in the above illustration may also be determined by operating conditions rather than by the stress imposed by the live load. If the package surface has an abrasive quality, the belting may be subject to excessive wear. If the package edges are sharp and the load is dropped onto the conveyor, the belting can be damaged. When deflectors are used and the belt is pulled to one side, the edge of the belt will tend to curl up unless it is thick enough to resist this action. For any or all of these reasons a thick belt should be used and four plies or more would be specified. Generally the belting should be no less than three plies thick. One- and two-ply belts are rarely suitable for package conveyor operation.

In the illustration given, the tensile strength of the belting will vary from 1,440# for a 24″ 3-ply unit to 3,600# or more for a 30″ 4-ply belt. In either case the available strength may be greatly in excess of the requirements, due to the live load on the conveyor. In the following descriptions of various kinds of belting, more data will be given on strength and application.

TYPES

The most common types of belting are: solid woven cotton, stitched canvas, rubber-impregnated, rubber-covered, and thin rubber. All belting will stretch as it conforms to the action over pulleys, and this initial lengthening will usually stabilize after a few weeks of operation. After this initial settling there is continuous movement due to atmospheric changes and variation in the live load on the conveyor. The amount of this stretch varies with the type of belt, as shown in the following descriptions.

Solid woven cotton belting is normally made in 3-ply and 4-ply construction. It is a light-duty belt and will stretch readily as live load is increased. The operating stretch amounts to 4 per cent of the belting length. The maximum operating tension is 20# per inch of width per ply.

Stitched canvas belting is a heavy-duty belt. The plies are stitched at close centers. It is normally made in 3-, 4-, and 5-ply construction. The duck is made in two grades of weight—32-ounce and 37½-ounce. The maximum tensions per inch of width per ply are 25# and 30# respectively. The stretch due to atmospheric and/or live load variation is 3 per cent.

Inner-stitched canvas belting is made in the 37½-ounce construction. It differs from the regular stitched canvas construction in having each pair of adjacent plies stitched together before they are assembled. This additional sewing increases its strength and its wear resistance. The permissible tension per inch of width per ply is 35#. The stretch of the belting will be 3 per cent of its length.

All of the cotton and stitched belts can be given neutral oil and paraffin treatments to minimize the effect of atmospheric changes. Flexible plastic coverings are also available where sanitary operating conditions must be satisfied. The plain or uncovered belts can be used on slider-bed construction as well as on roller beds. The loads can be readily deflected off the conveyor from uncovered belting. When loads are dropped onto the conveyor and/or are to be deflected, it is best to use the heavier-duty stitched belting. However, under severe abrasive conditions or where sharp objects are dropped onto the conveyor, the stitching may be cut; under such conditions it may be best to use a rubber-covered belt as described below.

Rubber-impregnated belting is composed of plies of duck alternated with thin sheets of rubber called "friction." The assembly of fabric and rubber is subjected to pressure and heat. The rubber is forced into the weave of the fabric where it is vulcanized into a tough, elastic bond. The belting is known as "friction surface rubber belting." The word "friction" in this phrase can be misleading—the surface of the belt is smooth and is suitable for operation over slider beds and for deflection of loads from the conveyor. Some belts are made with a strip of rubber tape over the butt joint if the outer layer is folded over the inner plies. If this strip is present, the belt should be installed on the conveyor so that the strip does not contact or rub on slider beds.

The rubber belts are made in 28-ounce and 32-ounce ducks. The maximum operating tensions are, respectively, 25# and 30# per inch of width per ply. Normal operating stretch will be about 1½ per cent, or half that of the stitched canvas belts. In addition to the advantage of more stability under humid operating conditions, the belt can be slit to a narrower width without affecting its tensile strength per inch per ply. (Cotton or canvas belting would fray or unravel if split.)

Rubber-covered belting is constructed of impregnated rubber belting with an extra layer of rubber vulcanized to the top and in some cases to the back or underside. The covers do not add to the tensile strength of the belting. A top cover may be used to absorb the impact of sharp objects or loads dropping onto the conveyor. Other top covers are vulcanized with special gripping designs permitting the conveyor to be installed at greater angles than are possible with uncovered belts or those with smooth rubber covers. The permissible angles will be covered later, in the discussion of inclined conveyors.

Belting with top cover only will operate satisfactorily over slider-bed conveyors. Loads, however, cannot be readily deflected from these belts. Some belts are completely covered (top, bottom, and edges), and this construction is normally used to protect against damage by liquids. A vulcanized splice is then used in place of the conventional mechanical splice to assure 100 per cent protection.

Thin rubber belting is similar in construction to the rubber impregnated belting described. The fabric and rubber sheets are very thin, and the thickness of the belt is about 25 per cent that of the regular belts. The tensile strength is about 6# per inch of width per ply.

The thin belts are primarily used in food-processing plants, pharmaceutical houses, and on comparatively short narrow conveyors handling light loads. The belting is very flexible and will operate over small diameter pulleys. Covers are available and the same limitations for use on slider beds, deflection, etc., given for conventional rubber-covered belting apply.

All rubber belts are available in natural and synthetic rubber construction for use where acids or oils are present.

All operating tensions or tensile strengths given above are considered maximum, unless the manufacturer authorizes a greater figure for a specific condition. All splices, as recommended by the belt maker, will permit stressing to the limits given.

Belting made with reinforcing members sewn or vulcanized into the body to increase tensile strength are normally not used in package conveyor design. Recent developments using extra-strong materials in the belt construction have resulted in a thin single-ply or "plyless" belt that has high tensile strength. This belt permits use of smaller pulleys than those required for conventional belting. The extreme flexibility, however, is a handicap in any operation requiring deflection of the load from the conveyor. Such belts also do not meet the recommended minimum of 3 plies for conveyor work but are suitable under some conditions.

Our coverage of package conveyors must include mention of the various forms of steel belts. Belting made of a band of thin stainless or plain steel is ideal for many special applications where conventional fabric or rubber belting cannot be used. Pulleys are comparatively large in diameter and the belt contact is 180°. High tension is maintained in the belting, assuring a smooth conveying surface. Stainless steel belting makes an ideal medium for sanitary handling in food-processing plants.

Other forms of steel belting employ wire mesh similar to wire fencing material, wire rods that are linked into a continuous band, articulated metal links forming a flexible band, etc. These latter belts may be combined with chains that become the driving medium. Other arrangements wrap the belting around special pulleys not unlike the design used for conventional canvas and rubber belting. Conveyors with these "open-type" belts are used in washers, dryers, and annealing furnaces, where all surfaces of the load must be equally subjected to the operation.

Conveyor Assemblies

HORIZONTAL

Figure 6–2 shows outlines of various horizontal belt conveyor arrangements. The various elements are identified by accepted nomenclature.

The arrangement shown in Fig. 6–2(a) is a simple one-way conveyor. The carrying belt may be supported by a roller bed or a slider bed. The snub pulley can be a heavy-duty roller if the belt tension does not warrant the greater capacity of a pulley. The takeup pulley may be manually adjusted or automatically operated. Belt tension, pulley sizes, types of drives, and takeup adjustment will be discussed in detail later.

The arrangement in Fig. 6–2(b) shows the most effective location for an automatic takeup. The adjustment in the regular takeup pulley, at the left in the illustration, may be very short and used only to assist in training the belting.

In the arrangement in Fig. 6–2(c) the drive is located in the return-run portion of the conveyor. This location is sometimes used for one-way service, when it is desired to have the end pulleys free of appurtenances such as drive and takeup accessories. This drive location is the most

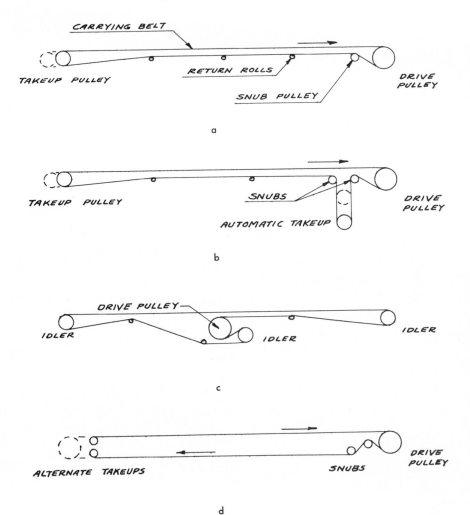

Fig. 6–2. Arrangements of horizontal belt conveyors. (a) One-way service. (b) One-way service. (c) One-way or reversing service. (d) Two-way service.

effective for reversing service. Takeup adjustment to compensate for belt stretch may be applied to any of the idler pulleys.

The arrangement in Fig. 6–2(d) shows a conveyor designed to convey loads in one direction on one strand of the belting and in the opposite direction on the other strand. The drive pulley should be located at the end pulling the greatest load, if live load differs on the two strands.

INCLINED

Figure 6–3 illustrates several arrangements of inclined belt conveyors. The arrangement in Fig. 6–3(a) shows the drive pulley located at the

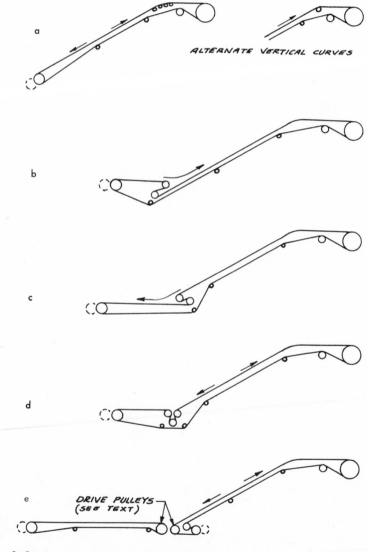

Fig. 6–3. Arrangements of inclined belt conveyors. (a) Up or down service. (b) Up service. (c) Down service. (d) Up or down service. (e) Up or down service.

upper terminal of the conveyor. In all conveyors the drive should be located at the point toward which the load is traveling. In a declined conveyor, however, the drive is located at the upper terminal although the load is *leaving* this terminal. This location assures that the belting will contact the pulley tightly. Two types of vertical corner are shown; the proper design of the corner depends on the package being conveyed. This feature will be discussed fully when vertical corners are covered later.

The arrangements in Fig. 6–3(b), (c), and (d) show alternate designs of inclines with built-in "tail belts." Tail belts are short horizontal sections of conveyors used to effect a smooth transfer of load from roller conveyors or other horizontal conveyors to the inclined sections. The horizontal sections are usually very short—probably no more than twice the length of the longest load being handled.

The arrangement in Fig. 6–3(e) shows an incline with a separate conveyor acting as a tail belt. In this design there is no limit to the length of the tail belt. It may be powered from the inclined conveyor; to do this a chain drive would connect the two pulleys indicated as "drive" pulleys in the illustration. The power required to drive the tail belt is normally small, and these drive pulleys can be of lighter-duty construction than the main drive pulley at the top of the inclined portion. If the tail belt is long and the power required to operate it is substantial, it will probably be more economical to treat the horizontal portion as a separate conveyor. In this case the pulley at the bottom of the incline can be a conventional idler. In either case the separate tail belt permits the use of more economical plain belting on this portion of the conveyor, and loads may be deflected if desired. Also, the horizontal conveyor can be operated at a speed other than the speed of the incline.

Engineering

BELTING AND MOTORS

The first step in designing the belt conveyor is to calculate the magnitude of the stresses in the belting, and the horsepower requirements. To assist in determining these values, the weights for conveyor components shown in Table 6–3 can be used. These weights are only approximate but, since anti-friction bearings are used for pulley shafts and in rollers, any slight variation in weight will have little effect on the final results. Also, the belting weight is normally much less than the weight of the live load so that any small discrepancy in belting weight has little bearing on the total stress and horsepower.

If the objects being handled are extremely light but a wide conveyor is required, the belting can readily outweigh the live load. This condition is not unusual, and when it occurs practically all the stress in the belting and all the power applied at the drive are needed to operate the empty conveyor. Sometimes it is difficult to detect any additional load on the motor as the light objects feed onto the conveyor.

Another point to remember is that minimum pulley diameters can only be determined after the stress in the belting is known; it is impossible to predetermine a more accurate weight of these components.

Table 6–3. Weights of belt conveyor components.

Width of Conveyor	Pulleys		Rollers		Width of Belt	Belting per Foot			
	Light Duty	Heavy Duty	Light Duty	Heavy Duty		Cotton, Canvas, or Rubber			Thin Rubber
						3-Ply	4-Ply	5-Ply	
6"	20	–	1.0	–	6"	0.6	0.8	–	0.3
8"	25	–	1.3	–	8"	0.7	1.0	–	0.4
12"	30	–	1.8	–	12"	0.9	1.2	–	0.6
18"	35	60	2.6	4.2	18"	1.2	1.6	–	1.0
24"	50	80	3.2	5.3	24"	1.8	2.7	3.0	–
30"	75	100	4.0	6.6	30"	2.2	3.4	4.0	–
36"	–	125	–	7.6	36"	–	4.2	5.0	–
42"	–	140	–	8.7	42"	–	4.8	6.0	–
48"	–	170	–	9.7	48"	–	5.4	6.8	–

Weight in Pounds

The drive requirements on package conveyors is small, and frequently fractional horsepower motors can be used. Except in unusual cases, nothing smaller than $\frac{1}{3}$ horsepower motor should be used, and many engineers feel that $\frac{1}{2}$ horsepower is a better minimum choice.

The frames that mount the bearings for pulley shafts are constructed of structural steel and therefore the alignment cannot be as accurate as that obtained with machined bases. Also, the power required to "break in" the belting can affect initial operation if the horsepower of the motor selected is figured too closely. Low voltage in the power line can also cause trouble if motor size is on the low side.

It is not suggested that belt conveyors should be over-motored to "play safe." This would be poor engineering practice. It is, however, good engineering to review the motor requirements of all belt conveyors in a system. If for example we find eight $\frac{1}{2}$-HP, ten 1-HP, three $1\frac{1}{2}$-HP, six 2-HP, and four 3-HP motors indicated, it would be advisable to standardize on a few sizes to simplify the stock of spare parts. In some plants only the 1-, 2-, and 3-HP motors would be considered, using the next larger motor for all sizes not carried in spare parts stock. In the interest of reducing the maintenance problem further, a similar review should be made of pulley sizes and belting widths.

If more accurate data on component parts weights are desired, the exact weights can be obtained from the manufacturer. Only the weight of revolving parts of rollers should be considered in the calculations.

The operating load or "effective pull" for a horizontal belt conveyor is calculated as follows:

Roller-Bed Conveyors
    Weight of all pulleys   ×   .02*   ......

Plus
    Weight of live load **
    Weight of all rollers
    Weight of all belting

                             ×   .05*   ......

           Total effective pull ....

Slider-Bed Conveyors
    Weight of all pulleys   ×   .02*   ......

Plus
    Weight of live load **
    Weight of carrying belt only

                             ×   .25*   ......

Plus
    Weight of return rollers
    Weight of return belt only

                             ×   .05*   ......

           Total effective pull ....

* 2 per cent friction for anti-friction bearings used on pulley shafts.

5 per cent friction for rollers (the 2 per cent used in gravity roller-conveyor calculations will not be sufficient when these rollers are used in belt conveyors because of the sagging of the belting between rollers). Also, increase this friction to 10 per cent if grease-packed bearings are used in the rollers.

25 per cent friction for all untreated, neutral, oil- or paraffin-treated cotton and canvas belting, and for friction surface rubber belting on galvanized or hot rolled steel slider plate.

** Live load cannot always be calculated as so many packages of a given weight handled per minute. In some arrangements the packages may be stored on accumulating conveyors in the system; therefore, at times, a solid train of packages needs to be handled by the conveyor.

The total effective pull, when multiplied by the speed of conveyor in feet per minute, indicates the horsepower required at the drive shaft.

Proper allowances must be made for the speed reduction efficiency, to determine the size of motor needed.

The effective pull on inclined conveyors can be calculated in the same manner as an equivalent length of horizontal conveyor; the product of the live load weight per foot of conveyor multiplied by the vertical rise in feet is then added. The effort needed to raise the weight of the carrying belt is offset by the downward thrust of the return belt.

If the conveyor declines, the live load moving down can readily exert enough effort to run the conveyor by gravity. The purpose of the belt conveyor, however, is to control the flow of packages. The reduction

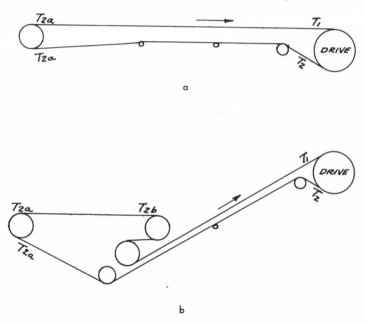

Fig. 6–4. Stress locations in belting.

gearing of the motor must be large enough to hold back the load. Also, if the conveyor is stopped, the speed reduction elements between the motor and the drive pulley must be strong enough to withstand the shock of stopping the conveyor. The motor on declined conveyors will usually then be the same as would be required if the conveyor raised the load.

A brake is normally required in the drive of inclined or declined conveyors to prevent the live load from moving the conveyor when it is stopped. On occasion a backstop is used on the drive shaft of inclined conveyors in place of a brake.

Having found the effective pull in the conveyor, the stresses in the belting and the sizes of pulleys can then be calculated. Figure 6–4 shows the various segments of belting that must be considered in these calculations. The maximum stress in the belting occurs at T_1, and the magnitude of stress varies as the degree of belting contact with the drive pulley changes. In most designs a 210° contact is possible. As will be seen in Table 6–4, the stress T_1 decreases as the degree of contact increases. Also, lagging on the pulley increases the grip on the belting and keeps the stress to a minimum.

Table 6–4. Ratio of stresses T_1 and T_2 for belt conveyors.

Degree of Belt Contact with Drive Pulley	Lagged Pulley		Bare Pulley	
	T_1	T_2	T_1	T_2
180°	1.50 EP	0.50 EP	1.85 EP	0.85 EP
200°	1.42 EP	0.42 EP	1.72 EP	0.72 EP
210°	1.40 EP	0.40 EP	1.67 EP	0.67 EP
215°	1.36 EP	0.36 EP	1.64 EP	0.64 EP
220°	1.35 EP	0.35 EP	1.62 EP	0.62 EP
240°	1.30 EP	0.30 EP	1.54 EP	0.54 EP

EP = Effective pull.

The minimum belting size can now be calculated by dividing the stress T_1 by the allowable operating tension per inch per ply of belting. The result is the minimum number of inch plies that will satisfy the requirements. Assume, for example, a conveyor with stress T_1 of 1,130#. The belting to be used must be 24″ wide and has a permissible operating tension of 25# per inch per ply. Dividing 1,130# by 25# gives 45.2 as the minimum number of inch plies needed. Since the belt is 24″ wide we find that 1.88 or a 2-ply belt would satisfy design requirements. A 3-ply belt would be used, however, because this is the minimum recommended for general conveyor service.

Stress T_2 is the slack side tension in the belting. This always is the difference between T_1 and effective pull, and it must be maintained to assure the proper belting contact with the drive pulley.

Other stresses—T_{2a}, T_{2b}, etc.—are normally not calculated, except on very long conveyors or where the belt direction is changed frequently over snub pulleys. The return belt weight riding over the return rollers increases the tension in the belting from T_2 to something greater, T_{2a}. On a conveyor less than 50 feet long this difference is small and can be ignored. Tension T_2 can then be used to calculate the load on the end or take-up pulley. If the conveyor is snubbed frequently as in Fig. 6–4(b), the gradual increases in belt tension from T_2 to T_{2a} and from T_{2a} to T_{2b}, etc., should be considered to determine accurate loading on the various pulleys. The increase from T_{2a} to T_{2b}, for example, is due to live loading as well as belt weight. If the intermediate is slider-bed construction, the increase may be substantial.

The increases in stress from T_{2a} to T_1 in Fig. 6–4(a), and from T_{2b} to T_1 in Fig. 6–4(b), are due to live loading and belting weight.

As the length of the conveyor increases and/or the live load per foot increases, it becomes more important to consider stresses other than T_1 and T_2 to obtain accurate snub and idler pulley loadings.

PULLEYS

It is advisable to use pulleys of as small a size as is compatible with the type of belting and the stresses in the belt. Not only is the small pulley more economical, but it will permit more satisfactory connections to other conveyors than would a large pulley. Manufacturers of belting are constantly improving the flexibility of their belts to prevent undue damage as the belts negotiate pulleys; the bonding of the several plies is strained as a belt bends around a pulley.

The following minimums apply to conventional cotton, canvas, and rubber-impregnated belting:

1. 3″ of pulley diameter per ply if belting is stressed to 60 per cent or more of its operating strength.
2. 2″ of pulley diameter per ply when belting is stressed less than 50 per cent of its capacity.
3. Between 50 per cent and 60 per cent loading, consider the need for long life vs. the need for minimum diameter pulleys.

The minimum diameter pulley for thin rubber belting should be about 4″ for each $\frac{1}{16}$″ of thickness.

No liberty with the above minimums should be taken without the approval of the belt manufacturer.

Take-up, snub, and idler pulleys are not required to transmit torque; rollers may therefore be substituted for pulleys if the loading permits. Pulleys are units with integral shafts rotating in bearings mounted on the conveyor frame. Rollers are units with bearings assembled in the roll and turning on fixed shafts. Standard rollers, as used to support the carrying or return belt, may have sufficient load capacity if the belt contact is small. This latter condition as well as other typical relations are shown in Fig. 6–5. All examples illustrated ignore the weight of the pulley or roller.

All drive, take-up, and snub pulleys should be crowned to assist in belt alignment. The type of crown shown in Fig. 6–6(b) has several advantages over the style shown in Fig. 6–6(a). Since the difference in diameter at the center of the pulley and the diameter at the edges is less than the pulley in Fig. 6–6(a), the belting is not subjected to as much distortion as it bends around the pulley. Also, if the pulley is fabricated from

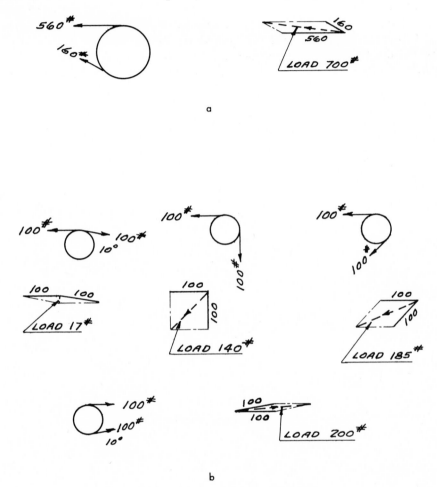

Fig. 6–5. Graphic calculations for loading on pulleys. (a) Typical drive pulley. (b) Typical snub, idler, or takeup pulleys.

a tube, the wall thickness of the tubing does not have to be as thick to assure a suitable thickness at the outer edges of the pulley face. A third advantage is that the crown shown in Fig. 6–6(b) has proven more effective in tracking the belting. In either cases the peaks of the crown can be rounded to eliminate any sharp apex.

As has been mentioned, the normal package belt conveyor is not heavily loaded (as compared to bulk material belt conveyors), and the shafts of pulleys can then be made of cold rolled steel. Rarely are ground and polished shafting or alloyed steels required.

Since pulleys are comparatively small in diameter, the hubs are frequently arranged in solid heads either formed integrally with the pulley or welded in place as shown in Fig. 6–6. Excessive deflection in the shaft will cause the hub mounting heads to flex as the pulley turns, and this reversal of stresses will result in fatigue failure of heads or binding of

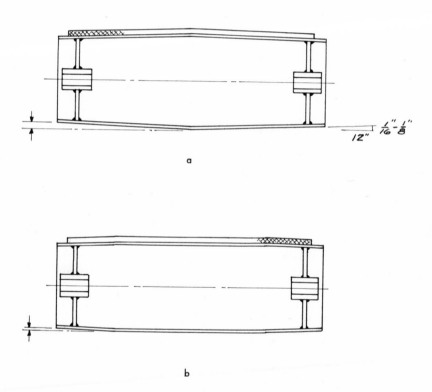

Fig. 6–6. Conveyor pulley crowns.

shafts in the bearings. Many engineers limit permissible stress in the cold rolled shafts to 8,000#. It has been found from experience that the use of this low stress protects against excessive deflection and allows for loss of strength when keyways are used. It would be well, however, to be certain that the angle of deflection on wide conveyors does not exceed the angle permitted by the shaft bearings.

All frames that mount the shaft bearings for pulleys should be equipped with means for adjusting the alignment of pulleys. This feature is essential to permit proper tracking of the belting. It is also necessary to adjust alignment of some rollers such as snub or return rollers. The brackets that support the fixed shafts of the rollers are usually equipped with slotted holes to allow for this adjustment.

Naturally, the conveyor frame must be installed plumb, and all rollers in the frame must be true and at right angles to the frame. The belting must be free of excessive camber. The latter can be checked readily by folding the belting back on itself after carefully cutting the belt for the splice. If, for example, a 24″ belt is to be installed on a frame with 25″ between sides, the camber should not exceed ½″.

Another precaution is to be certain that the pulleys are slightly above the level of the rollers or slider bed, intermediate to the pulleys. This is essential on slider-bed construction to prevent undue wear on the plate or belting, and overloading of the drive.

DRIVES

There are three general methods of reducing the speed between the motor shaft and the drive shaft:

1. Separate gear reducer coupled to the motor.
2. Geared head motor.
3. Drive pulley shaft-mounted reducer.

Some typical assemblies of drives are shown in Fig. 6–7. When a separate reducer is used, the motor is coupled to the reducer, and the slow speed shaft of the reducer is then either coupled directly to the drive pulley shaft or connected by roller chain drive. Further speed reduction is thus obtained. When the chain drive is used, the motor and reducer may be located on a support frame directly above or below the conveyor proper. The gearing in the reducer may be worm, spur, herringbone, or a planetary arrangement of gears.

Gearhead motors are available with various types of gear reductions. They may be coupled directly to the drive pulley shaft, or a chain drive can be used to permit flexibility in location of the gearhead motor.

The shaft mounted reducer is installed on the drive pulley shaft. A torque arm locks the reducer housing to the conveyor frame. In this arrangement the high-speed shaft of the reducer is usually connected to the motor by means of a V belt drive.

In many instances the type of drive is dictated by space limitations surrounding the conveyor. The most commonly used drives are the gearhead motor with worm gear reduction, and the shaft-mounted reducer.

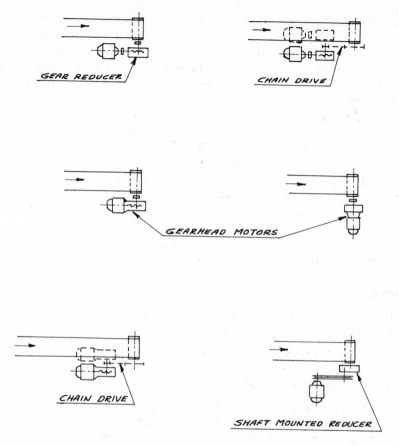

Fig. 6–7. Belt conveyor drive arrangements.

BELT ADJUSTMENT

As previously mentioned, all belting stretches and shrinks. The belting must be kept snugly in contact with the drive pulley, and this is accomplished by maintaining the slack side tension T_2.

The automatic takeup is the only *perfect* way of maintaining the proper tension in the belting. Manually adjusted screw takeups are more economical and will provide satisfactory operation under certain conditions, as outlined hereafter.

The first step is to determine the amount of adjustment that must be provided. The percentage of stretch given previously for the various kinds of belting will determine the amount of takeup pulley movement that should be provided. The wrap around the pulley should be 180° so that each foot of pulley movement will provide two feet of belting adjustment. It is unnecessary and often impractical to provide adjustment for the initial stretch as well as the normal change in belting length during conveyor operation. It may be necessary to remove a piece of belting and re-splice it a few weeks after the conveyor is started initially.

The T_2 tension can be maintained in several ways. The takeup pulley can be weighted so that gravity will provide the tension if a vertical automatic takeup is used, as shown in Fig. 6–2(b). The total weight of the takeup pulley and the auxiliary weights should be $2 \times T_2$ in this arrangement.

The automatic takeup pulley can also operate in a horizontal plane. When so arranged, counterweights are connected by means of an equalizing harness to the pulley shaft, pulley bearings, or a sliding frame mounting the pulley. In this case the counterweights must equal $2 \times T_2$ plus a certain amount to overcome the friction of the sliding parts.

The use of counterweights on the horizontal automatic takeup may prove to be an extravagant use of space. Pneumatic or hydraulic cylinders are often used to maintain the tension and provide a more compact assembly.

The use of springs for actuating the takeups is not recommended, because the travel is usually too great to permit constant tension in all positions.

At times the conveyor may be required to provide reversing service. In a reversing conveyor, the stress in the belting passing over the takeup pulley will alternate between T_1 and T_2 in magnitude, depending on direction of travel. The weight of the vertical takeup then must be calculated on the basis of $2 \times T_1$ to be effective. Obviously, such an arrangement is not ideal. Locating the drive in the center of the reversing conveyor does not improve conditions at the automatic takeup. If the reversing conveyor is very long, it is often more practical to use a drive at each end of the conveyor, with automatic vertical takeups at each drive. Each takeup is capable of exerting $2 \times T_2$ pull on the belting. The takeup at the drive not being used is then not strong enough to overcome the stress in the belting which is, say, T_{2a}, as shown in Fig. 6–4(a). The weighted pulley will rise in its sliding frame and remain in this upper position. The other takeup at the drive operating the conveyor is the effective takeup during that cycle of operation.

There may be other reasons for special treatment of the automatic takeup pulley. Limitations of available height may not permit sufficient travel of the pulley to accommodate normal "come" and "go" of the belting. Two adjacent takeups are then provided, each with a travel distance of half the total distance needed.

Another special arrangement may occur if the automatic takeup must be located at some point other than immediately after the drive pulley.

The weight then must be based on $2 \times T_{2a}$ or whatever tension exists in the belting at the location chosen.

When the conveyor is comparatively short, so that normal stretch does not amount to an appreciable footage, the automatic takeup is not necessary. All conveyors have return rollers spaced about 10'–0" between centers, and the belting sags or drapes between the rollers. The return belt is free to drop or rise in these loops, and the normal "come" and "go" that would occur in a twenty-four-hour period is absorbed in the loops. An ordinary screw takeup can be manually adjusted at infrequent intervals to maintain sufficient tension at the drive and insure good operation.

Table 6–5. Conveyor lengths vs. takeup adjustment.

		Maximum Conveyor Length Using Screw Takeups							
		12" Adjustment				18" Adjustment			
	Type of Belting	Actual Stress vs. Rated Capacity				Actual Stress vs. Rated Capacity			
		10%	25%	50%	100%	10%	25%	50%	100%
Indoors or Heated	Cotton	100'	75'	50'	40'	150'	100'	75'	50'
	Canvas	120'	100'	75'	50'	175'	150'	100'	70'
	Rubber	200'	175'	130'	100'	300'	250'	200'	150'
Outdoor	Canvas	90'	70'	50'	30'	150'	100'	60'	40'
	Rubber	120'	100'	75'	50'	175'	150'	120'	75'

The figures in Table 6–5 show the maximum conveyor lengths when manually adjustable takeups are used. The table is based on length adjustments of 12" and 18". These are standard lengths.

In the initial setting of the takeup pulley, only enough tension is put in the belting to insure good traction at the drive pulley. It will equal the calculated T_2 tension when the full complement of live load is on the conveyor. *There should always be a noticeable sag in the belting between return rollers* to permit normal shrinking and stretching without constant adjustment of the takeup pulley position. The conveyor must be observed regularly and the pulley position adjusted when necessary, to maintain the ideal operating conditions.

If the belting stretches so that T_2 tension is lost and the drive pulley slips, it will be noticed immediately: the conveyor will stop operating or become erratic in advancing the load. There is considerably more danger if the belting shrinks. The increased tension will not affect operation until it reaches the point where the belt parts, a pulley shaft breaks, or the pulley is pulled off its mounting. Conveyor frames have buckled under high belt tensions.

The manually adjusted screw takeup is not perfect, but it will give satisfactory service if properly applied and maintained. The screws providing the means for adjusting each bearing should always be in compression. They are fitted into the bearing mountings, and a pair of nuts at a vertical leg of the frame move the screw and bearing mountings as the nuts are turned. An alternate arrangement uses fixed position screws that turn in nuts fitted freely in the bearing mountings. As the screw is revolved, the nut moves along the screw, changing the position of the pulley in the frame. In either arrangement the two screws can be adjusted independently of each other. The only precaution is that the total adjustment must be the same on both sides of the conveyor, to assure continued proper tracking of the belting.

SAFE INCLINES

Most package or unit loads will negotiate inclines of 10° on plain cotton, canvas, or rubber-impregnated belting. The exceptions will be some cartons made of stock which is waxed or similarly treated to protect contents against moisture, and smooth-bottom wood or metal pans, boxes, or pallets.

When greater angles are encountered or where smooth-bottom loads are handled, special covers on the belting can be provided. Probably the most economical are the various types of patterned rubber covers available on rubber belts. Such covers will convey the average loads up inclines of 30° to 35°.

Cleats can be provided on any of the three types of belting, but the height or thickness of the cleats, in many cases, prevents the use of snub pulleys or rollers at the drive, and return rollers are often impractical. This limits the use of high or thick cleats to special-purpose conveyors. Where only slight slippage occurs, indicating that the conveyor is close to a critical angle, thin cleats made of pieces of belting, leather, or similar material may be sewn or otherwise fastened across the belting at, say, 3' or 4' intervals. Such cleats should not exceed ¼" in height, and the conveyor will operate satisfactorily using the standard snub and return roll construction. Reducing the spacing of rollers in the carrying bed or replacing rollers with a slider bed may also help to eliminate slipping of loads on the incline.

On all inclined conveyors for up or down service, it is important that the center of gravity be well within the base of the load. Figure 6–8 shows the recommended limit for safe handling. If the load contains a liquid in containers, the center of gravity must be carefully located. Also, many loads—for example, many crated or boxed appliances—have high centers of gravity. Stopping and starting the inclined conveyor may tip any load whose center of gravity drops through the unsafe area.

In the transition from the inclined portion to the horizontal section of a conveyor at the top of an incline, there are two types of "vertical corners," as shown in Fig. 6–3(a). The curved unit consisting of several rollers is used for all long loads and for any load where the center of gravity falls close to the safe limit, as shown in Fig. 6–7. Also, this type of transition should be used on all down service conveyors.

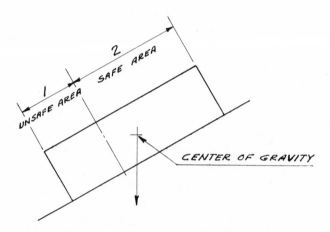

Fig. 6—8. Safe incline for loads on belt conveyors.

The single-roll vertical corner can be used for all short loads and for those where the center of gravity falls well within the safe area. The load will continue to ride up the incline until its center of gravity overbalances and it drops onto the horizontal section of the conveyor. This "slap" may be objectionable on long loads. The single-roll corner should not be used on down service, because the slap onto the declined portion may invite slipping if the angle of incline is near the critical zone.

DEFLECTORS

There are many types of deflector designs for diverting loads or packages from belt conveyors. The most common arrangements are shown in Fig. 6–9.

The simple bar or arm deflector shown in Fig. 6–9(a) may be fixed or hinged with the pivot located as shown. The arm of the deflector may be of any material and shape that offers the minimum resistance to the package sliding across its face. The belting on the conveyor can be any type except rubber-covered, although very light loads can be deflected from a smooth rubber cover if the angle of deflection is reduced to about 25°.

The package being deflected should have a length-to-width ratio of at least 1.5 to 1. A curved transition section in the arm, as shown in Fig. 6–9(b), will aid in deflecting packages that have a lower ratio of length to width. Square packages can be deflected, but they will tend to turn at the deflector; their relative position of travel can be changed when they enter the receiving conveyor. Reducing the angle of deflection will assist also when square or nearly square packages are being handled.

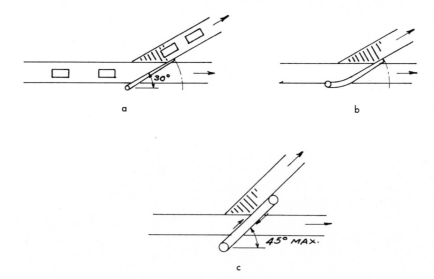

Fig. 6–9. Deflectors for belt conveyors.

The deflection action slows the forward motion of the package and, because this slowing process is not uniform even with identical loads, spacing cannot be maintained. This condition is illustrated in Fig. 6–9(a).

The speed of the belt conveyor should be 50 FPM minimum. Higher speeds will improve the deflecting action while slower speeds tend toward erratic action. Rollers or wheels can be used in the deflector arm to reduce friction, but the bumping of the leading corner of the package as it changes its position can be troublesome. Rollers or wheels make satisfactory deflecting arms if the load is circular or has well-rounded corners.

If the deflector arm is to be hinged, the movement may be manual or powered. If powered, the arm can be motor driven or operated by a hydraulic or pneumatic cylinder. In most cases the pivot point should be located as shown in Fig. 6–9(a).

Fig. 6—10. A series of deflectors on belt conveyor delivering to roller gravity accumulating lines. (Courtesy Lamson Corporation.)

A powered deflector such as is shown in Fig. 6–9(c) may be constructed of a vertical belt or slat conveyor. The speed of the deflecting conveyor should be proportional to the conveyor speed, to maintain spacing of the load reasonably well. At an angle of 30° the deflector speed should be 120 per cent of the main conveyor speed; at 45° it should be 145 per cent, etc. The powered deflector may be fixed or hinged.

In any of the designs illustrated, the package being deflected changes its position on the conveyor as it contacts the deflector. Therefore, it is necessary to have the packages spaced as they enter the deflecting zone. Special designs are available to remove loads closely spaced or even touching, but these units are pushers rather than deflectors. There are many types of pushers that can be used to divert loads from belt conveyors.

Very heavy loads that normally have high friction on the belting can be diverted, but, again, such deflectors require special design considerations tailored to meet specific conditions.

Special Applications

Figure 6–11 shows several types of special belt conveyor applications. Some are modifications of conventional conveyors; others are specially designed units that are available from manufacturers of paper-handling conveyors.

The belt conveyor shown in Fig. 6–11(a) is a two-way belt conveyor in which the bottom belt (normally the return belt) also conveys loads. The intermediates can be either roller-bed or slider-bed on both levels, or roller bed can be used on one level while slider bed is used on the other. The loads on the lower level must be deflected from the conveyor at the end of the travel. With this construction the return belt cannot sag between rollers, and the normal operating "come" and "go" of the belting cannot be absorbed as previously described for one-way service. It is desirable, therefore, to include an automatic takeup in the conveyor. The takeup may be incorporated in one or both of the idler pulleys shown to the left of the illustration rather than where it is pictured. It may be horizontal in movement or a gravity operated vertical takeup may be used.

The design in Fig. 6–11(b) shows a belt conveyor with the return belt snubbed under rollers on the bottom level. This arrangement utilizes the return belt to drive the rollers and makes a "live-roll" conveyor of the bottom level. The service is two-way but the direction of travel is the same on both levels. (Chapter 7 covers the details of live-roll conveyor construction.) The comments given above regarding automatic takeup for the two-way belt conveyor apply here.

The conveyor shown in Fig. 6–11(c) is known as a "squeeze" belt and is used to transport papers and similar materials. The "squeeze" belt will also convey small unit loads that will not be damaged by the pressure generated between the two belts as they negotiate changes in direction at pulleys and rollers. The arrangement can take any form. Two separate belt conveyors can be arranged to travel over common pulleys and rollers. In this manner sufficient pressure is developed between the belts to convey the articles. On vertical runs the idler rollers or pulleys are arranged in a zigzag manner, as illustrated, to assure firm contact between the two belts at all times. Up service is shown in the illustration, but down or even reversing service is possible. The belting used is usually a narrow, rubberized, thin belt, and the return sections of belting can be arranged

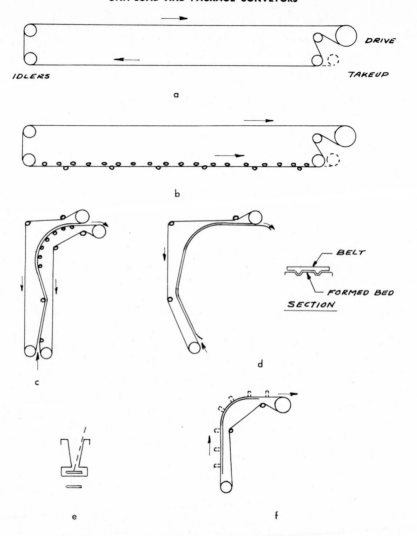

Fig. 6–11. Special belt conveyor arrangements.

to absorb the small amount of operating stretch and shrink that occurs. Spring tension takeups can be used because of the small movement.

A similar paper-handling conveyor known as a "drag" belt is shown in Fig. 6–11(d). The belting in this conveyor is a specially molded rubberized belt, one type of which is shown in the cross-section. The belt is held firmly against the formed bed, and the paper is dragged along by the moving belt. Unlike the squeeze belt, this conveyor is limited to conveying single sheets of paper or very thin bundles of papers that will not be damaged by the action between the belting and the fixed bed. It can also be arranged to carry papers up or down and to give reversing service.

The conveyor shown in cross-section in Fig. 6–11(e) is known as a V belt conveyor. It may be single-lane, as shown, or multiple-lane for serving several points. The conveyor travels horizontally and is ideal for transporting messages, cards, tickets, etc. It is used frequently to deliver messages from several operators to a dispatch or service desk.

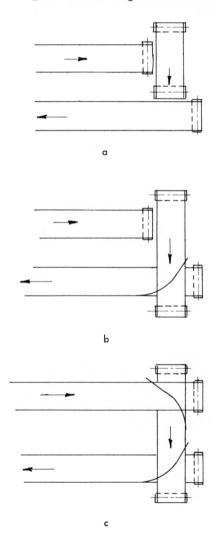

Fig. 6–12. Belt conveyor connections. (a) Belt-to-belt transfer. (b) Belt-to-belt and one deflector. (c) Two deflectors.

All belt conveyors used to convey sheets of paper must be well grounded to avoid accumulation of static electricity. Discharge wiper fingers against the belting will help to carry off the charge that builds up as the belting rubs over the slider bed.

The belt conveyor shown in Fig. 6–11(f) uses permanent or electromagnets installed in the bed of the conveyor. Ferrous articles can then be conveyed by the conveyor up steep inclines or vertically as shown in the illustration.

Curved belt conveyors, usually made in 90° units, are also available. The belting can be stitched canvas, rubber-impregnated, or steel belting of the mesh, rod, or link type. These conveyors are used as connections between conveyor lines arranged at 90° or 180° to each other. Also, the curved belt conveyors can be arranged to form a completely circular manual picking or sorting station.

Straight belt conveyors are also used to connect conveyor lines where the normal roller or wheel gravity conveyor curves are not practical. When the straight conveyor is used for connections, the usual arrangement is one of the three shown in Fig. 6–12.

7

Live-Roll Conveyors

Live-roll conveyors are similar in construction to gravity roller conveyors but they have power applied to the rollers. The power can be obtained by driving each roller with a motor in a manner very much like that used by the familiar conveyors in rolling mills, to pass the metal slabs and sheets between mills. Rarely, however, is this type of live roll used in unit or package handling.

The most common driving medium is belting or chain, as shown in Fig. 7–1. The arrangement using a belt snubbed under the rollers is shown in Fig. 7–1(a). Two arrangements with chain as the driving means are shown in Fig. 7–1(b) and 7–1(c). These three forms of live-roll conveyor will be discussed fully later in this chapter.

The live-roll conveyor has two main functions. First, it is used as an accumulation or storage conveyor. The belt driven type shown in Fig. 7–1(a) is the only one that should be used for this purpose. The other major use of the live-roll conveyor is for transportation when the nature of the load being handled is such that the more flexible and more economical belt conveyor is impractical. The load may have abrasive or sharp corners that would damage belting. There may be occasion to transfer heavy loads to and from the conveyor, and lifting fingers can then be applied under the load between the rollers to effect the transfer.

The rollers are usually normal or heavy-duty types and range between $1\frac{3}{4}''$ and $2\frac{9}{16}''$ in diameter. Shaft sizes are either $\frac{1}{2}''$ or $\frac{3}{4}''$ ($\frac{7}{16}''$ or $1\frac{1}{16}''$ hex).

The load is propelled along the conveyor by the friction between the revolving rollers and the load. With the steel roller normally used, this friction will vary from 25 per cent for loads with smooth bottoms to 40 per cent for loads such as cartons. Slippage between the load and the surface of the roller is noticeable when the conveyor is started or stopped. There is also some slip during normal travel, though it may be difficult to detect with the naked eye. It is for these reasons that the live-roll con-

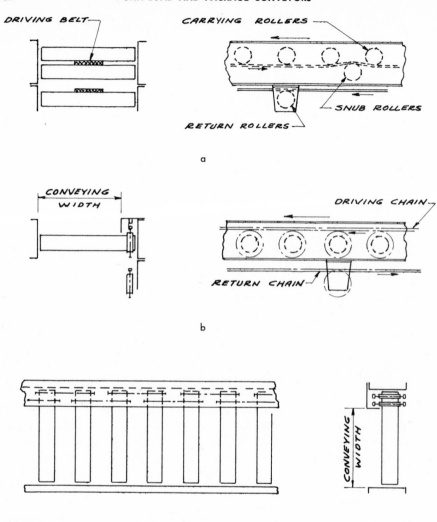

Fig. 7–1. Live-roll conveyor designs. (a) Belt drive. (b) Continuous chain. (c) Roll-to-roll chain drive.

veyor is never used where exact timing or spacing of loads is essential. Coverings may be applied to the rollers to increase friction but rarely is such a procedure economical.

Transportation Live Roll

Conveyors used for transportation only may be driven by belting or by chain.

BELT DRIVE

When belting is used it is snubbed under the carrying rollers by snub rolls spaced as shown in Fig. 7–1. This illustration shows two out of every three rollers positively driven. Closer snub spacing to drive every roller or greater spacing to drive two out of four rollers may be used. At least two rollers under the minimum length load should be driven.

It is essential that the snub rolls be vertically adjustable so that the degree of snub can be regulated. Only enough snub to assure travel should be used. Excessive snubbing increases the power required at the drive. Generally a snub height of between 25 per cent and 50 per cent of the belting thickness is sufficient.

The driving belt is shown in the central position in Fig. 7–1(a), but it may be located anywhere along the width of the conveyor. Regardless of position, the belt will be subject to contamination from small items that may fall through the roller spacing. If operating conditions are such that this condition exists and the belting is likely to be damaged, a chain drive should be substituted for the belt. The spaces between the rollers is then clear and debris can drop through harmlessly.

The rule for minimum spacing of carrying rollers is the same as given in Chapter 5 for gravity roller conveyors. The belt part of the conveyor is treated as a regular belt conveyor with minimum pulley diameters, snub pulley arrangement at the drive, and takeup design, all subject to the same treatment as given in Chapter 6.

The effective pull of the belt driven live-roll conveyor is calculated in the same way as a roller-bed belt conveyor, except that the roller friction is increased from 5 per cent to 7 per cent to allow for the extra pull required by the snubbing of the belting. The formula becomes:

$$\begin{array}{lll}
\text{Weight of all pulleys} & \times \quad .02 & \ldots\ldots \\
\text{Plus} & & \\
\quad \text{Weight of live load} & & \\
\quad \text{Weight of all rollers} & & \\
\quad \text{Weight of all belting} & & \overline{} \\
& \times \quad .07 & \ldots\ldots \quad \overline{} \\
\quad\quad \text{Total effective pull} & \ldots\ldots\ldots\ldots\ldots\ldots\ldots
\end{array}$$

The width of the belting is not dictated by load width except that it cannot be wider than the width of conveyor required by the load. The belt need be only large enough to withstand the maximum stress T_1. The magnitude of T_1 is dependent on the degree of wrap on the drive pulley and the type of pulley, as shown in Table 6–4.

Since the belting should be flexible to withstand the snubbing action, it is good practice to use as thin a belt as possible. The best belting is stitched canvas or impregnated rubber. If, for example, the stress T_1 is 890# and the belting has an operating tension value of 30# per inch per ply, the requirement will be for a belt with 29.67-inch plies. An 8″-wide 4-ply belt or a 10″-wide 3-ply belt would satisfy requirements. It would be advisable to use the 10″-wide 3-ply belt if conveyor width permits.

On transportation live-roll conveyors the load is never stored; means can therefore be employed to improve the traction between the belting and the roller surfaces. As explained previously, it is not good practice to use excessive snubbing to obtain traction. A stitched canvas belt can be given an added treatment to increase surface friction, and rubber belts can have thin rubber covers applied. The treatment in the canvas belt is usually a bituminous compound; in addition to the "tacky" result, the treatment also protects the fabric against the shrinking effect of high humidity. The live-roll conveyor rarely requires automatic takeups because the normal sagging of the return belt between idlers is sufficient to compensate for operating stretch and shrink.

CHAIN DRIVE

If it is decided to use a chain driven conveyor, the continuous chain with tangential contact with the sprockets can be specified. The sprockets should have special teeth to reduce the tendency of the chain to lift off the sprockets. A holddown track is recommended, as shown in Fig. 7–1(b). This construction requires very careful assembly and millwrighting.

The roll-to-roll drive shown in Fig. 7–1(c) consists of complete chain drives between rollers. The need for a holddown track and return chain support is eliminated, but the friction loss in each drive limits the number of rollers that can be driven from one drive position. Good practice indicates that 70 driven rollers is the maximum that should be used in one run of a conveyor.

In either design the number of drives needed can be halved by placing the drive motor in the center of the conveyor run. It is then possible to drive two lengths of conveyor from the same motor. The chain pull in each run is kept to the permissible limit and, in the case of the roll-to-roll drive, 140 rollers may be powered from one motor.

In both chain driven designs shown, the sprockets are mounted on the roller. This permits use of standard rollers with fixed shafts mounted in the conveyor frame. It is possible to use a roller with a revolving shaft and the sprocket(s) mounted outboard on the shaft. This latter construction, however, requires shaft bearings in the conveyor frame—a costlier design.

The chains best suited to the standard live-roll conveyor are either ⅝″- or ¾″-pitch roller chain. The working load or permissible chain pull at various conveyor speeds is shown in Table 7–1.

Table 7–1. Working loads for chains on live-roll conveyors.

	Maximum Working Load – Pounds			
	Conveyor Speed – FPM			
Chain Pitch	To 30	31-60	61-80	81-100
5/8"	870	760	610	400
3/4"	1,200	1,060	850	850

The formula for determining the pull in the chain with the continuous chain drive design is:

$$P = L \times N \times f$$

where

L = total load per driven roller (live load plus roller weight).
N = number of driven rollers.
f = factor per Table 7–2. (The weights of rollers with sprockets are also shown in Table 7–2.)

In calculating the chain pull for the roll-to-roll drive design shown in Fig. 7–1(c), the formula becomes:

$$P = \frac{L \times N \times f}{0.98^n}$$

where

L = total load per driven roller.
N = number of driven rollers.
f = 0.03 for free-running bearings
   0.06 for grease-packed bearings.
n = number of chain drives.

The 70th power of 0.98 equals 0.24 plus. This means that the chain pull in the final drive of a 70-roller conveyor run will be about four times the pull required by the weight of live load and roller, without considering efficiency of the main motor drive.

The roller to which the main drive is connected in either design is subjected to two forces. One is the maximum pull in the chain driving the rollers, and the other is imposed by the drive connection to the motor. This latter force is generally at some angle other than the horizontal pull of the chain driving the rollers. This combination of forces frequently requires a roller of heavier construction for the drive.

The belt driven live-roll conveyor permits loads to be diverted or deflected from either side of the conveyor by arranging the rollers in high position in the frame. With either of the chain driven types, the load can be diverted from one side only.

Table 7–2. Factors for calculating chain pull on live-roll conveyors.

Roller Diameter and Shaft	Factor f		Weight Roller and Sprocket – Pounds						
	Free-Running Bearing	Grease-Packed Bearing	Conveyor Width – Inches						
			12"	18"	24"	30"	36"	42"	48"
1-3/4" to 2" 7/16" hex – 1/2"ϕ	0.05	0.08	4	5	5	–	–	–	–
2-1/2" 7/16" hex – 1/2"ϕ	0.04	0.08	6	7	8	9	10	11	12
2-9/16" to 3" 11/16" hex – 3/4"ϕ	0.05	0.08	9	12	14	16	19	21	24

Accumulating Live Roll

As stated previously, one of the chief functions of a live-roll conveyor is its ability to accumulate or store loads. The action of accumulating loads presents a problem of pressure on the loads as they collect and particularly on the load that is contacted by the stop mechanism. Many modifications of live-roll design are used as accumulators. In Chapter 5, figures have been given to permit calculation of the pressure developed on a gravity line when used for storage. (Also see Table 15–1 for more detailed factors in calculating the pressure.)

The roller slat conveyor, discussed in Chapter 8, is an ideal accumulating conveyor but, because of its high cost, it is used only when more economical units are not practical.

By far the most popular accumulators are the various forms of live-roll conveyors. The following descriptions are not given in any order of preference. Each type has favorable features that make it acceptable for a particular purpose, provided the limitations can be tolerated.

On any belt driven live roll, the powered rollers force the load forward by virtue of the friction between the roller surface and the bottom of the load. The belting used should have a low friction surface. Untreated or neutral oil-treated stitched canvas belts are ideal for this service. Uncoated rubber-impregnated belts are equally suitable. The rollers that are under the load when it is stopped will stop turning, and the belting will slide under the stalled rollers.

The friction between the load and the driven roller is naturally dependent on the nature of the bottom of the load. Also, because the belting has a low friction surface, it is not positive in its action against the roller. Since so many unknown factors are involved, the magnitude of the pressure in a blocked mass of loads has to be determined in laboratory and field tests.

On a level belt driven conveyor, where at least two driven rollers are under the minimum length load, the pressure against the stop mechanism will be 9 per cent of the total weight of the mass of accumulated loads.

This comparatively low friction is the result of minimum adjustment of the snub rolls. The snub rolls should be lowered until none of the carrying rollers is turning. The snubs are then gradually raised until just enough pressure is exerted to move the load when it is free to travel. As soon as the load is blocked, stopping the rollers under it, the belting will slip under the rollers. The average carton, wood box, or metal tote pan has a higher friction factor against the roller than does the belt surface. The only force, then, that exerts pressure in the mass of blocked loads is the result of the belting sliding against the rollers.

The pressure exerted by accumulated loads on the above type of live-roll conveyor can be reduced by installing the conveyor at a slight angle of decline. The grade should be such that the load will not travel by gravity. Snub rolls are spaced every 5′ or 10′, and this will result in four or two driven rollers at every 10′ of conveyor length.

When the stop mechanism is actuated, the part of the load resting on the rollers over the snubs will exert pressure due to the belting sliding under the driven rollers. All other rollers, however, are dormant; they do not add to the pressure. The mass of accumulated loads has a natural force because of the angle of decline, but this force is reduced or offset by the friction of the bearings in the rollers.

The pressure exerted by the accumulated load on the declined conveyor with snub rolls spaced at 5′ or 10′ centers is:

$$P = 0.02W \text{ plus } \frac{Wv}{100}$$

where

W = total weight of accumulated load in pounds.
v = factor due to drop or grade (see Table 7–3).

As will be seen from the values v in Table 7–3, the grade of 0.25″ approximately balances the resistance of the bearing friction in the rollers.

Table 7–3. Factors for calculating pressure on live-roll conveyors.

Grade — Inches per Foot	v	Grade — Inches per Foot	v
0.10″	0.0	0.60″	3.1
0.20″	0.0	0.70″	4.0
0.25″	0.2	0.80″	5.0
0.30″	0.6	0.90″	5.8
0.35″	1.0	1.00″	6.6
0.40″	1.4	1.50″	10.6
0.50″	2.5	2.00″	14.7

This, then, is the ideal grade to keep the pressure to a minimum, provided the load will not travel by the force of gravity. Also, any grade of 1″ per foot or greater will produce a pressure equal to or in excess of the pressure created by the accumulated load on the conventional level conveyor described above.

When the stop mechanism is released, the driven rollers will drive the mass forward. At the grade of ¼″ or less, the start of movement gradually reaches the conveyor speed. At greater grades the natural downward force aids in starting the mass, and movement is almost instantaneous. On these greater grades, however, the force created by gravity can propel the loads faster than desired. Therefore, the best grades are those from 0.20″ to 0.35″ per foot of conveyor.

It is assumed that the accumulated loads will not stay on the conveyor for long periods, and therefore very little settling of soft bottom loads over the rollers will occur. If the operation is such that loads may be stored for prolonged periods, it would be well to use a greater grade to aid in starting the mass from rest after the stop mechanism is released.

SPECIAL ACCUMULATORS

A level live-roll conveyor equipped with a specially constructed belt is another type of accumulating conveyor that produces little pressure against the stop mechanism. The belting, which is a normal 3- or 4-ply stitched canvas or rubber belt, is constructed with spaced pads as shown in Fig. 7–2. The length of the pads and the spacing in the belt are optional.

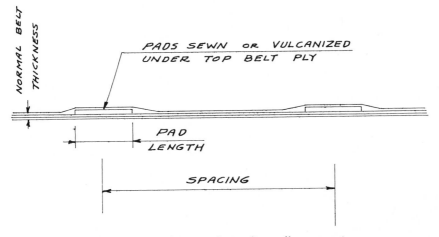

Fig. 7–2. Special accumulating live-roll construction.

The snub rolls are arranged so that the normal thickness of the belting does not contact the carrying rollers. As the pads advance, they contact the carrying rollers and advance the load a distance of about twice the length of the pad. When the loads are free to travel, they (the loads) advance along the conveyor in a series of start and stop motions. If the conveyor operates at 60 FPM and pads 24″ long are spaced 15′ apart, the load movement will be about 16 FPM. If the load is 18″ long, the system will have a maximum capacity of about 10 loads per minute vs. the maximum possible 40 loads on a conventional conveyor operating at the same speed.

When the stop mechanism is actuated, the loads will begin to accumulate. However, in a mass of loads the pads create pressure only every 15′ (using the above example). If the conveyor is 100′ long, only six pads can be in contact with the rollers at any time. The resulting pressure created is then equal to an amount that would be created on a conveyor six times 24″ or 12′ in length with all rollers driven. The pressure in this case would be 9 per cent of the total weight of load that could be accumulated on a 12′-long conveyor. Care must be used in setting the snub rolls so that the padded segments contact the rollers very lightly, as described previously.

In this design the cost of the specially constructed belt must be considered. Also, the limited capacity for a given belt speed may be objectionable. The need constantly to start the loads from rest, with resulting lag in reaching full speed, is the reason that the load movement can only be approximated at twice the length of the pad.

When the stop is released, the loads will discharge from this conveyor at spaced intervals instead of in a steady stream as is the case in conventional conveyors.

Another form of live-roll conveyor designed for accumulation employs special carrying rollers. The roll tubing ends that receive the bearings are concentric, but the center portion of the tubing is eccentric in form. (See Fig. 7–3 for a graphic description of this design.)

The short radius of a driven roller momentarily loses contact with the belting as the load is traveling, but the momentum of the moving load plus the fact that all of the driving rollers under the load are not likely to lose contact at the same instant keep the load moving.

When the stop mechanism is actuated and the loads come to rest, the belting turns the rollers under the load only until they reach the non-driving position, with the short radius of the eccentric clearing the belt. When a full complement of loads has been accumulated, all of the carrying rolls have stopped, with the roller clearing the driving belt. This then results in zero pressure in the mass, assuming of course that the conveyor is level.

It is obvious that with this design the release of the stop mechanism does not automatically start the accumulated loads flowing, as is the case with the previously described units where some pressure is constantly maintained. Two methods can be used to restart the flow of loads by re-establishing roller contact with the belting. The first method is to move the mass of loads backward a few inches. This turns the rollers about 90°, and they again contact the belting, setting the loads in motion.

The action of moving the accumulated loads a few inches, to establish roller contact with the belting, can be incorporated in the stop mechanism. If the mechanism retracts out of the conveying path to release the loads, the stop, as it retracts, can move in an arc and so push the mass

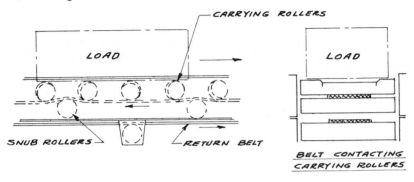

a

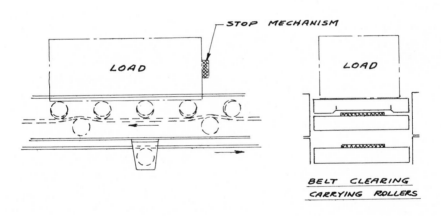

b

Fig. 7–3. Special accumulating live-roll conveyor. (a) Moving load. (b) Blocked load.

back before it clears the conveyor. If a metering type of stop is used, the metering conveyor can start in the reverse direction and then change over to the normal or forward direction. (All types of stop mechanisms are covered in Chapter 15.)

The second method that may be used to restart the flow of loads employs a special belt of a construction somewhat similar to the belt shown in Fig. 7–2. In this case, however, the pads need be only about 3″ long, and they can be widely spaced. Only three pads are required in the endless belt to assure that at least one pad travels through the conveyor at all times. With this arrangement the continuously traveling pads maintain some pressure in the mass of accumulated loads. The rollers are momentarily turned to belt contact by the pad, and they will revolve under the blocked load until the short radius of the roller again clears the belt. In this way, first one and then the next load in line will exert some pressure. The amount is small and will be equal to about half the weight of a single load. The magnitude of this pressure decreases as the pad moves toward the rear of the accumulated loads, the pressure being gradually absorbed in the mass of loads.

Fig. 7–4. Live-roll accumulating conveyors employing eccentric rollers. (Courtesy Mathews Conveyer Company.)

As the loads are released and exit from the conveyor, they will be spaced somewhat because the pads cause first one and then the next load to start. This spacing is small, amounting to about half the load length. The flow from this conveyor differs from the flow from the conveyor previously described, because here the pad simply starts the rollers in motion and thereafter the belting keeps them revolving. In this case, then, with a load length of 18″ and a belt speed of 60 FPM, the exit rate will be about 27 loads per minute until all accumulated loads are discharged.

Another type of accumulating conveyor, while not truly a "live-roll" conveyor, does use standard rollers or wheels as the load-supporting medium. A detail of this conveyor is shown in Fig. 7–5.

The rollers or wheels support the load. The top of the belting is slightly above the level of the rollers or wheels, exerting only enough force to drive the load forward against the resistance of the bearing friction in the rollers or wheels. The detail of the relief mechanism has been simplified in the illustration to show the principle involved. As a load

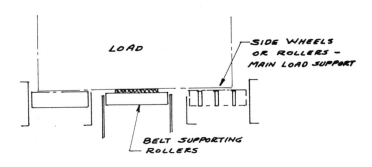

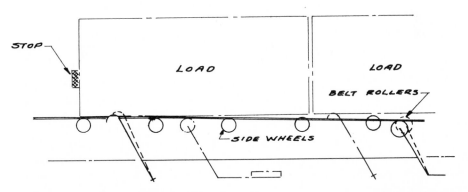

Fig. 7–5. Special accumulating design. The belt-supporting roller under the second load is dropped out of contact by a trigger depressed under the first load.

travels, it depresses the wheel of the forward lever. This action is transmitted to the rear arm that carries the belt-supporting roller. The roller is lowered and the belting in back of the load is dropped below the driving level. As a load comes to rest against the stop mechanism, it depresses the belt-supporting medium in back of it. The next load then stops in back of the first load but, as the belting has been lowered, the load is stationary and exerts no pressure against the first load. Each subsequent load depresses the belting in back as it joins the train of accumulated loads.

With this conveyor the pressure against the stop mechanism is confined to the pressure exerted by the first load only. The pressure will be small—about half the weight of the unit-load weight.

The spacing of the series of relief mechanisms is arranged to accommodate the length of the load. Loads should therefore be of uniform length to obtain the desired results.

Impact on Accumulators

In the foregoing descriptions of accumulating conveyors no reference has been made to impact against the stop as the first load comes in contact with the stop. If loads travel on the conveyor in the normal manner, they will be spaced and the impact will be a series of shocks as each load joins the mass of accumulated items. The magnitude of impact force against the stop gradually decreases as the mass of loads increases. If, however, loads enter the conveyor in solid trains, the solid group of loads striking the stop or other loads already at rest may require shock-absorbing features built into the stop.

The impact force as well as the pressure built up in an accumulator line may be sufficient to damage the loads. Load-to-load contact or load contact with the stop must be analyzed. The front of a carton may be depressed as it is forced against the stop mechanism. When the stop is released, the carton may regain its original shape and appear to have satisfactorily withstood the pressure and/or impact. However, the contents of the carton may have been damaged, even though the damage may not be apparent from the external appearance of the carton.

Loads being accumulated at any one time should be of reasonably uniform size and ruggedness. Mixed loads of widely varying size or weight should not be accumulated together. A narrow load mixed with larger units may be skewed on the conveyor and may jam between guards or be forced off the conveyor if guards are not provided. A light load can be crushed between heavy loads.

The power required to operate any of the accumulator conveyors described should be based on the effective pull in the belting required to convey the loads. In all of the designs mentioned, the pull in the belting is not increased when the loads are blocked. The belting is either allowed to slip under the rollers because of a very light snub roll adjustment; or, in the conveyor using eccentric rollers or the one using pressure relief arms, the belting is relieved of contact when the loads are blocked.

The effective pull is calculated in accordance with the formula given previously in this chapter for belt driven live-roll conveyors. In the case of the accumulating conveyor where load-supporting rollers or wheels are not driven by the belting, some reduction in the power requirements is possible. The belt conveys the load, but the rollers or wheels are turned by the load and therefore their weight must be considered. The belting, however, is not snubbed under the rollers, and 5 per cent friction can be used here in place of the 7 per cent given in the formula.

It is possible to remove manually a load from the group of accumulated loads because the pressure is comparatively low. Such an operation is more readily performed on the units using eccentric rollers or where the belting is relieved of contact with the load.

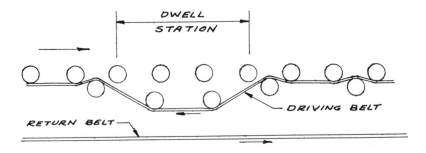

Fig. 7–6. Dwell station live-roll conveyor design.

The regularly snubbed belt type and both of the chain driven conveyors are unsuitable to accumulate loads. Pressures would be excessive and the power required to drive the conveyors under blocked-load conditions would be prohibitive.

The conveyor equipped with eccentric rollers can also be used on a production line where momentary operations are to be performed on the load without removing it from the conveyor.

An operator can readily stop a load, and the rollers under it will quickly stop rotating, permitting work on the load while it is standing still without being restrained by the operator. When he has completed his work, the operator gives the load a slight push and the rollers are again put into operation and take the load away.

The regularly snubbed belt type can also be used for similar work by equipping the conveyor with "dwell" stations like the one illustrated in Fig. 7–6. The belting is snubbed out of contact with the carrying rollers, and all loads stop in the idle roll or dwell station. Work can then be performed, and upon its completion the load is pushed ahead onto the next group of driven rollers.

Inclines and Diversion

The positive drive provided by the regularly snubbed belt type or either of the chain types permits the conveyor to negotiate inclines. Obviously the softer the bottom of the load the greater the angle of incline can be. Cartons have been successfully conveyed up 12° angles while smooth-bottom loads may be limited to half that grade. The angles are limited by the tendency of the load to slip on the rollers when starting from rest.

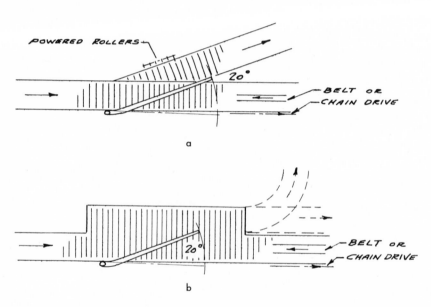

Fig. 7–7. Deflectors for live-roll conveyors.

As mentioned previously, loads may be deflected or diverted from the positive driven types of live-roll conveyor. Figure 7–7 shows two of the most popular deflectors. The simple fixed or pivoted bar can be used, as shown in Fig. 7–7(a), but the maximum angle of deflection is 20°. The driven rollers of the main conveyor do not have sufficient grip on the bottom of the average load to assure complete discharge. Therefore, it is usually necessary to power the first few rollers in the receiving conveyor.

The deflector arrangement shown in Fig. 7–7(b) provides extra-wide rollers in the deflecting area. The belt or chain that drives the regular width rollers also drives the wide ones. The 20° deflector bar diverts the load from the main line into the parallel path provided by the wide rollers. Once in this auxiliary path, the load discharges over the end to the receiving conveyor.

The deflectors will not divert square or nearly square loads. The most common square load handled by live-roll conveyors is the pallet. Such loads may weigh several tons and are best diverted from the conveyor by transfers operating at right angles to the conveyor travel. Transfers are covered fully in Chapter 15.

The live-roll conveyor is ideal for handling metal drums and barrels. The recessed heads on such items concentrate all the weight on a small ring that would damage the belting on a belt conveyor. Any other load, where the weight is concentrated on similar narrow perimeters or runners, can be successfully handled by the live roll. The only restriction is that the bottom of the load be flat and free of any projection that would make it unsuitable for handling on roller conveyors.

Wood pallets, on which an occasional loose nail or splintered board could cut belting, can also be handled on the live roll. If a nail should project, it may retard the travel of the pallet but no damage is likely to occur to the conveyor.

8

Chain Conveyors

Many conveyors use chains as the propelling or conveying medium. Some play such a prominent part in unit- or package-conveying systems that they will be covered in separate chapters. The others are grouped for discussion in this chapter.

Slat Conveyors

The slat conveyor is one of the oldest forms of conveyor. It consists of two strands of chain with slats mounted on chain attachments, as shown in Fig. 8–1. Figure 8–1(a) shows the roller chain with A-type attachments to which the slats are attached. Cross rods are shown between the chains. These rods extend through the chains at the roller centers and protect against tipping of the chains due to the eccentric load on the links.

Figure 8–1(b) shows a chain with flanged wheels in place of rollers. Cross rods are also used here. The flanged wheel chains are usually used in heavy-duty service.

In Fig. 8–1(c) the chain is equipped with K-type attachments. Here the slats extend over the chain and the load is distributed evenly on the links. Cross rods are not necessary with this construction. The return strand of conveyor, however, must slide on a series of runners. This design should be used only on short conveyors.

The chains normally used are 3″, 4″, and 6″ pitch with either malleable iron links or straight or formed steel links. Typical chains are shown in Fig. 8–2. The straight side bars are steel while the formed side bars may be steel or malleable iron.

The A and K attachments are shown with one mounting hole in each attachment. Standard attachments are also available with two mounting holes each. The cross rods may be specified at each chain link or, on lighter-duty conveyors, they can be at every other link, every third link, etc.

The slats may be wood or metal. Metal slats are usually made of formed or structural members. Reinforcing ribs may be required on wide conveyor slats.

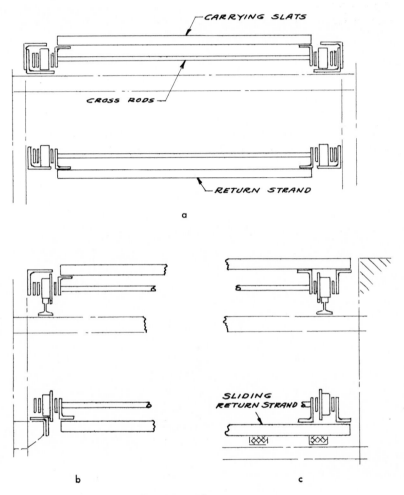

Fig. 8–1. Slat conveyor.

The slat conveyor is used when a large variety of loads are to be conveyed. Such items include reels of wire or fencing; bundles of shovels, rakes, etc.; heavy castings, or any other load that cannot be successfully handled on belt or live-roll conveyors. The conveyor can be installed in a trench so that the top of the carrying slats is flush with the floor. The

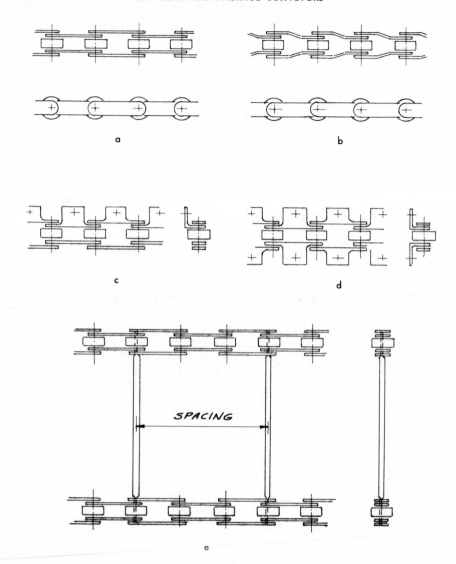

Fig. 8–2. Chains for slat conveyors. (a) Straight side bars. (b) Formed side bars. (c) A attachments. (d) K attachments. (e) Cross rod attachments.

slow speed at which the slat conveyor is normally operated makes it possible for foot traffic or trucks to cross the conveyor while it is conveying spaced loads.

The slats are full width with only ¼″ to ½″ open space between. With a 6″-pitch chain, the slats can be 5¾″ or 5½″ wide. The length of the slat forms the width of the conveying surface. If the conveyor is level and then curved to an incline, the space between slats usually has to be the full ½″ to allow clearance as slats negotiate the transition.

In calculating the power required to operate a level conveyor or the level portion of a conveyor, use the following:

          Weight of all sprockets   × 0.02   ......

Plus

          Weight of live load
          Weight of all chain
          Weight of all slats

                               ×   Factor f ......

          Total pull ....

The friction factor f depends on the diameter of the roller or wheel in the chain as follows:

$$f = 0.20 \text{ for } 1\tfrac{1}{2}'' \text{ to } 2'' \text{ diameter roller}$$
$$= 0.15 \text{ for } 2\tfrac{1}{2}'' \text{ diameter roller}$$
$$= 0.12 \text{ for } 3'' \text{ diameter roller}$$
$$= 0.10 \text{ for } 4'' \text{ diameter roller}$$

On inclined conveyors the carrying strand and the return strand must be calculated separately. The formula becomes:

Weight of all sprockets   × 0.02   ......

          Turning effort ....

Weight of live load   ......
Weight of carrying strands of chain   ......
Weight of carrying slats   ......

          Total carrying load L ....

$W = L \times$ sin of angle   ......
$W_1 = L \times$ cos of angle   ......
$W_2 = W_1 \times$ chain factor f ......

Weight of return strands of chain   ......
Weight of return slats   ......

          Total return load R ....

$w = R \times$ sin of angle   ......
$w_1 = R \times$ cos of angle   ......
$w_2 = w_1 \times$ chain factor f ......

Total pull for up service:

$$P = \text{turning effort} + W + W_2 + w_2 - w.$$

Total pull for down service:

$$P = \text{turning effort} + w + w_2 + W_2 - W.$$

The total pull is halved to determine the pull in each strand of chain. As in belt conveyors, if the down total pull P is a minus value indicating that the live load will operate the conveyor by the force of gravity, it should be treated as a plus value to insure a drive strong enough to control the flow.

The angles of incline can be increased by adding cleats or hold-back bars on the slats to prevent the loads from slipping. The center of gravity will limit the angle of incline.

ROLLER SLAT CONVEYORS

If, in place of wood or metal slats, conveyor rollers are used between the chains, the unit is known as a roller slat conveyor. In this design the cross rods are spaced at every link and become the axles for the rollers. The chain pitch is determined by the required centers of rollers.

When conveying loads the rollers do not revolve and become the carrying bed. When a stop is introduced, however, the rollers turn freely under the blocked load. Very little pressure is created in the blocked loads or against the stop. The pressure amounts to about 1.5 per cent of the weight of the total mass. The unit is often used as an accumulating conveyor for fragile loads and where instant starting of load movement, after release of the stop, is important. The accumulated loads discharge from the conveyor in a solid train.

Since the rollers are free to turn, the roller slat conveyor can only be installed horizontally. The power needed to operate the conveyor is calculated as follows:

         Weight of all sprockets $\times$ 0.02   ......

Plus

         Weight of live load
         Weight of all chain
         Weight of all rollers

                     $\times$ Factor f ....

       Total pull ....

Chain friction factor f is as given previously. The total pull is halved to determine the pull or stress in each strand of chain.

TRACTION BARS

The roller slat conveyor can be modified by adding traction bars under the rollers, forcing them to revolve while the chain is advancing them. These modifications take two forms. In the first type a bar is installed at a selected point or points in the length of the conveyor. A section through the conveyor showing the bar is illustrated in Fig. 8–3. The traction bar must be carefully adjusted so that it contacts the rollers but does not elevate the carrying run enough to lift the chains off the tracks or rails. The face of the bar contacting the rollers should be covered with a reasonably high-friction and soft material such as spongy rubber or plastic.

The surface of the rollers as they contact the traction bar will have a speed twice that of the chain advancing the rollers. If loads are spaced,

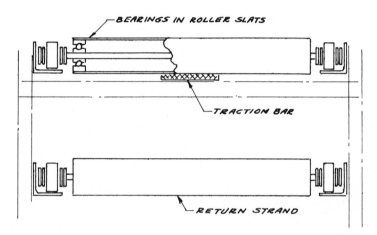

Fig. 8–3. Traction bar for roller slat conveyor.

say, 24″ centers on the free portion of the conveyor, they will increase to 48″ centers upon entering the area of the traction bar. This increase in spacing permits deflection of loads from the conveyor in the high-speed area.

The second modification consists of a traction bar or bars throughout the length of the conveyor. A section through this type of conveyor is shown in Fig. 8–4. Here the carrying run and the return run may be supported entirely by the traction bars. The face of these bars should be covered with a firm, reasonably smooth material such as a piece of rubber conveyor belting. If the bar is not covered the wear on the roller tubing will be excessive.

In this latter modification, a plain chain can be the propelling medium. Rollers in the chain would serve no useful purpose. Normally any chain should be operated at moderate speed to assure long life. The actual conveying speed of this design is twice the speed of the chain, and increased capacity can be obtained with nominal chain speed. Power required to

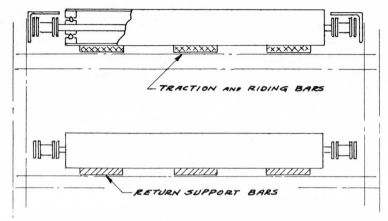

Fig. 8—4. Multiple traction bar for roller slat conveyor.

operate this type of roller slat conveyor is based on the chain pull derived from the following formula, multiplied by the speed of the chain:

Weight of all sprockets   × 0.02   ......
Plus
Weight of live load
Weight of all chain
Weight of all rollers

$$\overline{\times\ 0.08^*}$$ ....

Total pull ....

* Friction factor shown is for rubber belt surface.

Crossbar Conveyors

The crossbar conveyor consists of two strands of chains with spaced bars or rods supported between the chains. Figure 8–5 shows two typical forms of this conveyor.

The conveyor shown in Fig. 8–5(a) is used to handle parts through various dipping operations. A typical arrangement is illustrated. The bars may be fixed in the chains, and the parts to be processed can be hung on and removed from the traveling bars; or the bars may be portable, with pocket attachments on the chains to receive them. In the latter case the items to be handled are attached to the bars, and the complete assembly is then set into the pocket attachments.

The arrangement in Fig. 8–5(b) shows flexible fabric pockets attached to the fixed bars between the chains. The conveyor may have vertical and horizontal sections as shown. This conveyor is used extensively at docks to facilitate loading and unloading boats. The vertical leg can be lowered into the holds of the ship. It is frequently called a banana conveyor because it is popular for handling stems of bananas at dockside. The flexible pockets are ideal for handling fragile and/or odd-shaped loads that are difficult to convey satisfactorily on other types of conveyors.

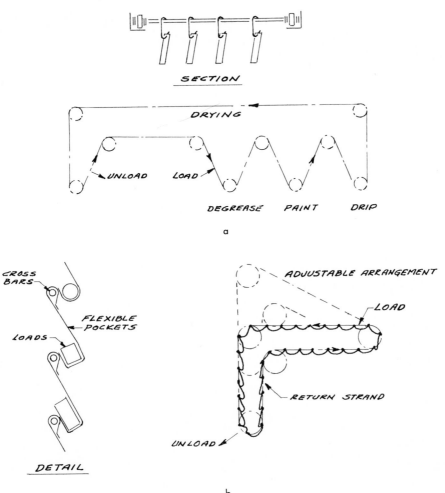

Fig. 8–5. Crossbar conveyor designs.

The friction of the roller chain used in the crossbar conveyor depends on the chain roller diameter as given previously in the formula for chain pull on slat conveyors. When the direction of travel is changed frequently, as in the case of the dipping conveyor in Fig. 8–5(a), it is advisable to calculate the chain pull progressively. The pull can be determined in the first segment of conveyor; this pull is then increased by 5 per cent before adding or deducting the pull in the next segment. The magnitude of the pull in the chains at the final segment before the drive sprocket will be more realistic. In the dipping conveyor, as with any type of conveyor having declined sections, a careful analysis of loading conditions is necessary. In many operations the inclined portions of the conveyor can be fully loaded, while the declined sections may be empty or lightly loaded. The force of gravity then will contribute very little if anything to reducing the final pull. An assumption that the entire conveyor is fully loaded may result in a figure that is erroneous.

Pusher-bar Conveyors

Another form of crossbar conveyor is the pusher-bar conveyor, shown in Fig. 8–6. The crossbars are fixed in the strands of chain and push the load along or up a bed arranged below the chain line. The bed may be slider-type or may be equipped with a series of rollers to reduce friction.

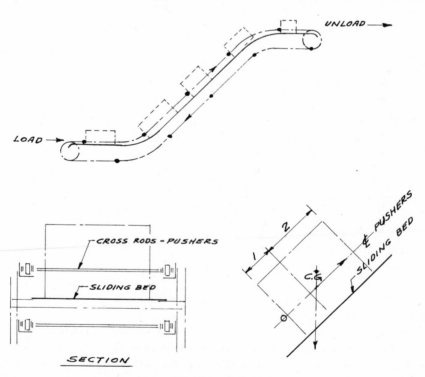

Fig. 8–6. Pusher-bar conveyor.

When rollers are used, the transition curve from the lower horizontal section to the inclined section is usually slider construction to provide smooth travel for square-cornered loads such as cartons, boxes, and tote pans.

An escapement device is provided at the lower or loading end to automatically feed one load into the space between pusher bars. The angle of incline can be great on this type of conveyor because the height of the pusher above the bed will prevent tipping, as illustrated in Fig. 8–6. Note that the center of gravity falls in the unsafe area at the bed level but within the safe area at the chain or pusher-bar level.

To assist in calculating the pull in the chains of the conveyor, use the following frictions to determine the magnitude of loading at the pusher bars:

    0.40 for cartons on steel slider bed.
    0.30 for wood container on steel slider bed.
    0.25 for steel container on steel slider bed.
    0.02 for any load on standard roller bed.

Round loads such as drums, barrels, etc., can be handled on pusher-bar conveyors. The round loads are rolled on runners or skids that are substituted for the roller or slider bed on conventional conveyors. The pusher bars are equipped with wheels to allow the rotating load to turn freely. With such loads the conveyor is never declined unless provision or allowance is made for impact of the load's rolling until it strikes the pusher bar ahead.

Car-type Conveyors

Car-type conveyors are those where a series of cars are attached to and propelled by endless chains. They are used to convey loads that cannot be handled on other types of conveyors because of the nature of the bottom of the load and/or because an operation to be performed in transit would damage belting or rollers on belt, roller, or live-roller conveyors. The path of travel may take several forms, as shown in Fig. 8–7.

The unit shown in Fig. 8–7(a) is a straight run of conveyor with the return strand below the carrying strand. With this arrangement the cars are mounted on flanged wheels that operate on rails or structural angle tracks. The chain, being a propelling medium only, can be plain link-type. Rollers in the chain are not required. When a single strand of chain is used, as shown, it is necessary to equip the ends with curved guides to prevent tipping of the cars and to assure proper feed onto the return tracks. Two strands of chain may be used, and the cars are then guided over the ends by the chain sprockets.

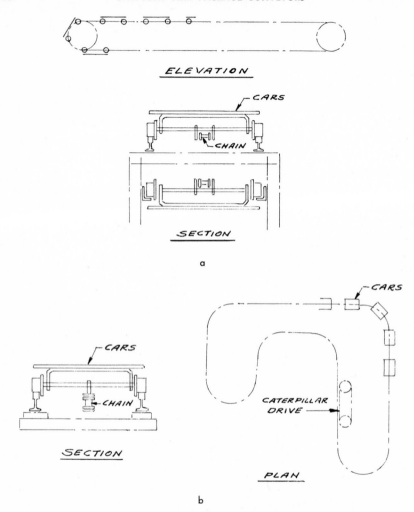

Fig. 8–7. Car-type conveyor arrangements.

In the design shown in Fig. 8–7(b), the cars travel in an endless loop. The radii of the turns in the loop are relatively large, to allow for smooth operation. The chain is powered by a caterpillar drive. Since sprockets are not used at the turns, the chain is guided around by curved segments equipped with closely spaced rollers. The friction loss at the roller turns, increasing the chain pull, can be calculated as 3 per cent for 45° and 5 per cent for 90° or greater turns.

Car conveyors can operate continuously and are used for transporting loads through various operations such as handling flasks through the pouring and cooling in a foundry, assembly of parts and testing of the assembled unit, etc. Specially shaped cars to accommodate rolls of paper, rolls of metal, etc., are used to handle these items into storage and out to the production lines.

The type shown in Fig. 8–7(a) frequently is programmed to stop at intervals so that machine or assembly operations may be performed on the unit being conveyed. When machine operations are performed, the load is mounted in a fixture that is attached to the car.

Rolling- and Sliding-chain Conveyors

Rolling-chain conveyors use two strands of chain with the load carried directly on the rollers in the chains. Two sections through a typical conveyor are shown in Fig. 8–8: one is for rigid, solid-bottom loads, and the

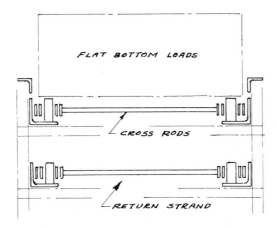

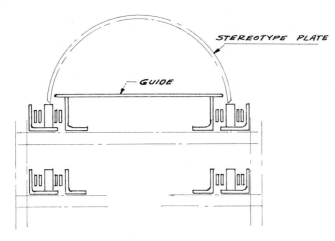

Fig. 8–8. Rolling-chain conveyors.

other is for special loads such as the stereotype plate shown. As in the case of the roller slat conveyor with traction bars, the load is conveyed at twice the speed of the chain.

A modification of the rolling-chain conveyor is shown in Fig. 8–9. Here a series of pairs of wheels that rotate on non-rotating axles are connected by chains. The chains are only the propelling medium, and plain chain can be used. The friction of the wheels on the tracks depends not only on the wheel diameter but also on the type of bearing in the wheels. If wheels are equipped with anti-friction bearings, the rolling friction may be as low as 2 per cent. The cross section in Fig. 8–9 shows the

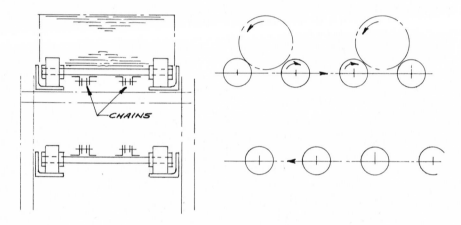

Fig. 8–9. Modified rolling-chain conveyor.

conveyor handling rigid-bottom loads, while the side elevation shows how the conveyor may be adapted to revolve round loads while in transit. The latter arrangement is frequently employed when the inside of barrels or drums is to be coated or otherwise treated. Painting of the outside is possible, provided the narrow unpainted band left by the turning wheels is not objectionable.

Sliding-chain conveyors employ plain chains that slide on a track or in a trough. Figure 8–10 shows a typical cross section through the conveyor. Two strands of chain are shown in the illustration, but multiple strands of more than two are frequently used when loads are heavy or when loads vary greatly in width. A wear strip is shown in the channel track. Wear strips are advised, as they can be readily replaced when necessary. Hard wood makes an acceptable strip; some plastics are available that require little or no lubrication; metal wear strips should be of alloyed material to assure that the replaceable strip will wear before the chain links wear. A friction factor of 0.35 should be used unless the type

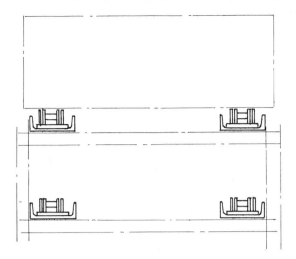

Fig. 8–10. Sliding-chain conveyor.

of material used justifies another figure. Lubrication is always used in or on the track unless specifically banned.

A chain having a large contact surface should be used. This not only reduces the unit pressure on the track but presents a greater area to the load and so reduces possible damage.

The chief use for the sliding-chain conveyor is the handling of raw material in bales, bundles, crates, etc.

Fig. 8–11. Special sliding-chain adaptation for unloading entire truck trailer of pallet loads. (Courtesy Alvey-Ferguson Company.)

Flat-top Chain Conveyors

Flat-top chain conveyors come in a variety of top plate shapes. The three basic designs are shown in Fig. 8–12. The designs in Fig. 8–12(a) and 8–12(b) are primarily for light loads and are frequently used in bottling houses, dairies, and canning plants at fillers, cappers, and label-

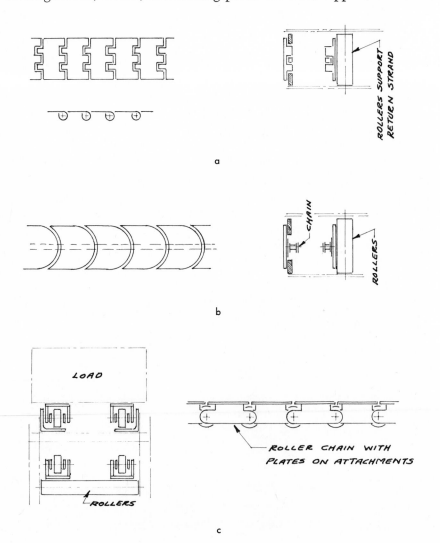

Fig. 8–12. Flat-top chain conveyor.

ers. The design in Fig. 8–12(c) is usually used with two or more strands of chain, to convey heavy loads.

The top of the chain shown in Fig. 8–12(a) is pierced and formed to make the male portion of a hinge at one side and the female at the other. When coupled, the completed chain forms a continuous conveying chain. The loads can readily be transferred onto and off the chain from the sides. The tops or platforms slide on tracks while the return strand is carried on spaced return rollers. The hinge projections below the tops fit into specially grooved wheels or sprockets at the drive and takeup ends of the conveyor. No conventional chain is required.

Fig. 8–13. Flat-top chain conveyor in automotive plant. (Courtesy Rex Chain-belt Inc.)

The unit shown in Fig. 8–12(b) has crescent-shaped top plates that are attached to the side links of a plain chain. The arrangement of the chain below and the shape of the top plates permit this conveyor to turn corners of small radii. Wheels guide both the carrying and return strands of chain at the corners. The return strand is supported on spaced rollers. This design will convey the same loads as the straight conveyor in Fig. 8–12(a). Loads can be diverted from and fed onto the carrying surface.

The flat-top chain illustrated in Fig. 8–12(c) consists of plates attached to the side links of roller chain. The chains are usually arranged in pairs and will convey heavy, firm-bottom loads. The return strands of chain are supported on rollers. The capacity of this conveyor is limited only by the type of roller chain to which the flat tops have been attached. The friction of the chain on the tracks depends on the diameter of the rollers in the chain, as shown in the formula for slat conveyor chain pull.

Special Arrangements

There are many combinations of chain conveyor and roller conveyor that are designed to meet special requirements. Two of the most popular arrangements are shown in Fig. 8–14. The design in Fig. 8–14(a) uses a loop of standard roller conveyor with a pusher-type chain conveyor providing the power to propel the loads. In the arrangement shown in solid lines, the loads enter the loop, by manual assistance, just ahead of a pusher attachment. The loading operation can be automatic with the aid of an escapement timed to the spacing of the pushers. The chain may advance the load to a predetermined point where it is stopped while work is performed on the load. Or the operation can be continuous and advance the loads through packing, weighing, and sealing operations. When the load reaches the end of the run, it is pushed out onto the discharge section of roller conveyor.

The loop of roller conveyor may be closed, as shown by the dotted lines. In this case the chain attachment is normally coupled to a pallet or open container, which is pulled rather than pushed around the closed loop. The conveyor is then used to handle material between machine operations. The items being conveyed are placed on the pallet or into the containers.

In either the open or closed loop, it may be necessary to increase the distance between the parallel lanes to a point where a sprocket drive is not practical. A caterpillar drive is then used and curved tracks guide the chain around the 90° corners.

The arrangement shown in Fig. 8–14(b) is used in assembly operations. The two parallel lines of roller conveyor support the load, while the trolley-type chain conveyor pushes the load. At the end of the conveyor line the chain conveyor declines into a pit in the floor and returns above the floor again at the beginning of the line to engage loads entering. In a typical installation the bottom of a shipping crate, acting as a pallet, is placed on the conveyor line. The product is gradually assembled on the pallet, and passes through test, inspection, and final packing operations.

In either case, similar service can be performed by tow conveyors (see Chapter 10), but in many instances the combination of roller and chain is more practical. One advantage of the combination is the low (2 per cent) friction of the roller conveyor. Another is that trucks or wheel-

mounted pallets or containers can be eliminated. The floor in the building area may not be suitable for truck operation.

The load on the pushers will be 2 per cent of the live load. The reac-
tion of the pusher load on the chain depends on the pusher design. The
guide and support wheels used on the chain shown in Fig. 8–14(a) can

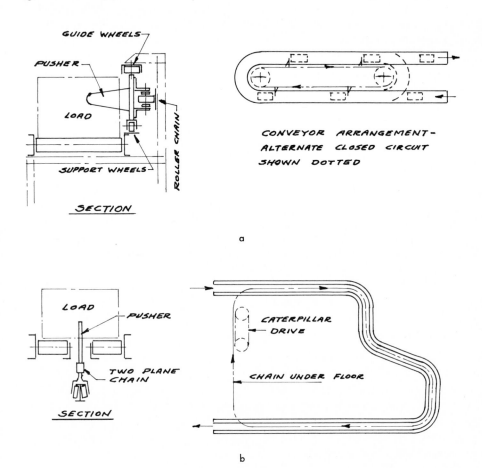

Fig. 8–14. Combination pusher-chain and roller conveyor.

be assumed to have no greater friction than the roller in the chain.
Therefore the frictions shown previously for various diameter chain
rollers should be used. Also, use a friction factor of 2 per cent for the
trolleys shown in the combination system in Fig. 8–14(b). The friction
loss at the roller turns that guide the chain at corners can be calculated
as 3 per cent for 45° and 5 per cent for 90° or greater turns.

General Considerations

LUBRICATION

When roller-type chain is used, it is essential that care be taken in lubricating the chain. Only enough lubrication to service the sleeve bearings of the rollers should be applied. If they are overlubricated, the excess collects in the chain tracks and invites the rollers to slide rather than turn. The sliding friction on a greasy or oily track will often be less than the turning friction. Sliding will result in flat spots on rollers and the chain is soon useless. Proper maintenance assures many years of chain service. Some chains are available with roller bushings that require no lubrication. The use of such chains is advised if they meet all other operating conditions.

SPEED

Chain conveyors can be successfully operated at very slow speeds. Assembly operations being performed frequently require speeds so slow that movement cannot be detected readily. In the event of a jam in the system, the normal overload in the motor control may not act in time to prevent damage. Therefore, on chain conveyors where the chain cannot slip (as can belting on the pulley of belt conveyors), it is advisable to provide some form of mechanical cutout. Such a device is essential on very slow-speed conveyors.

WORKING LOAD

It is possible that the conveyor length and/or the loading is such that the calculated chain pull exceeds the working load recommended by the chain manufacturer. The recommended maximum should never be exceeded. If it is not practical to use a stronger chain, it may be possible to introduce auxiliary drives. If the conveyor has many sprockets because of frequent changes in direction of travel, or if caterpillar drives are used, several drives can be coupled. They should be located at points just before the stress in the chain reaches the allowable limit. Multiple drives can sometimes be synchronized by the use of high slip motors. In other cases variable speed drives are used with automatic speed controls incorporated.

TAKEUPS

The takeups on chain conveyors need be only long enough to adjust for stretch in the chain due to wear at the chain joints. The amount of movement in the takeup is usually enough to remove one or two pitches of chain. Twelve inches of movement is usually the maximum required. Automatic takeups are rarely needed. However, if it is essential to maintain a tight chain at all times, the various types suggested for the belt conveyor can be used. Since the travel is very short, springs may be used with success.

At times the chain is equipped with attachments whose centers must be maintained. When this condition exists, it is necessary to provide takeup adjustment long enough to at least accommodate a full attachment space. When such long takeup adjustment is needed, an automatic takeup will probably be required to assure a tight chain at all times.

9

Trolley Conveyors

The overhead trolley conveyor is probably the most versatile conveying unit available. It can negotiate horizontal turns and elevate or lower loads while maintaining spacing and control over speed. It is frequently used to bring the load down to a working level and then elevate it over aisles until the next working area is reached. The conveyor can circulate and so keep a constant, moving supply of material available at work stations. In this way material is kept in live storage, avoiding the necessity of frequent handling into and out of storage.

The conveyor can handle a great variety of loads. Light or heavy items, large or small items, and fragile or rugged items can be handled on the same conveyor at the same time. The material being handled may be hot or cold, and it may pass through washing, painting, and baking operations. The conveyor can also be used as a tow conveyor, as covered in Chapter 10.

Trolley conveyors take many forms. The most popular are those with two-wheel trolleys operating on I-beam track. The trolleys support the chain which connects and propels them. The load may be suspended directly from the trolley as indicated in Fig. 9–1.

One modification of this standard construction uses steel cable in place of the chain. Sections of cable connect the trolleys. Buttons are attached to the ends of the cable sections, and these buttons bear in pockets in the halves of the trolley body.

The design using chain permits the use of caterpillar drives on the straight runs or sprocket drives at corners. Horizontal changes in direction may utilize sprockets, wheel, or roller turns. The permissible pull in the chain varies with the radius of horizontal turns and vertical bends, as given later in this chapter. Takeups can be arranged to permit removal of sections of chain. Normally, the takeup adjustment need be only enough to permit removal of two pitches of chain, i.e., one center link and one pair of side links.

When cable is used, the drive is a sheave-type wheel with pockets in the rim to clear the trolleys. The radius of all turns is limited by the type of cable and the clearance around the cable at the trolleys. Takeups must be arranged to remove elements of trolley spacing. The normal maintenance and inspection of cable for broken wires must be followed. "Stretch" is practically nil, for there are no moving parts to wear. All wear is at the buttons or beckets in the trolley pockets.

Many "light-duty" trolley conveyor designs are available. Small trolleys, using wheels of the type used in wheel gravity conveyors, operate over a T-bar track. The chains can be link-type similar to the standard

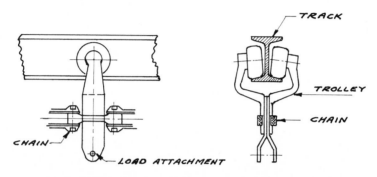

Fig. 9–1. Trolley for overhead trolley conveyor.

chains, coil link chain, or cable. Other designs use a chain with wheels built into the chain. The wheels are alternately horizontally and vertically mounted. The chain then is guided in round or boxed-type tracks around turns and vertical curves. Sprocket-type drives are usually used on light-duty conveyors.

The standard overhead trolley conveyor uses 3″-, 4″-, and 6″-pitch two-plane chain. The chain pins vary in diameter, affecting the strength of the chain. The standard construction of chain is shown in Fig. 9–2.

The allowable pull in the chain is limited, due to the bending of the side of the center link as it bears against the rollers in a horizontal turn, the bending moment on the chain pin, and the wear on the I-beam track at vertical curves. For these reasons the allowable pull should be limited to the values shown in Table 9–1. The table shows different values for various radii of horizontal turns as well as the minimum radii of vertical curves for different trolley spacings. Under favorable operating conditions, the lower values can be increased, but the pull shown for 48″ or larger radius turns should not be exceeded on multiplane service.

These chains are used in other conveyors such as drag conveyors, sliding chain conveyors, straight assembly lines pulling or towing fixtures and

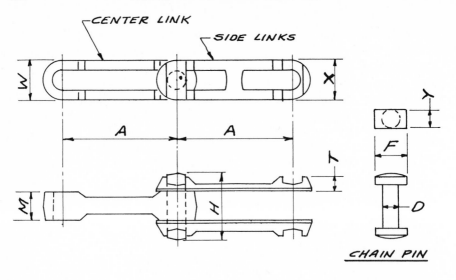

CHAIN NUMBER	INCHES									WEIGHT PER FOOT POUNDS
	A	D	F	H	M	T	W	X	Y	
348	3	1/2	3/32	1 27/32	13/16	13/32	1 1/16	1 1/16	17/32	2
458	4	5/8	1 7/32	2 1/4	1 1/64	15/32	1 13/32	1 3/8	21/32	3
468	4	3/4	1 1/16	3 9/32	1 5/8	5/8	1 7/8	1 7/8	25/32	7.5
658	6	5/8	1 7/32	2 1/4	1 1/64	15/32	1 13/32	1 3/8	21/32	3
678	6	7/8	1 7/8	3 1/8	1 5/16	3/4	2	2	15/16	6.5

Fig. 9–2. Overhead trolley conveyor chains.

dollies, etc. When used in such monoplane conveyors the normal factor of safety of 6:1 or 8:1 can be applied against the ultimate strength shown, to arrive at an acceptable allowable pull or working load.

Chain Pull

As in any package conveyor, it is good practice to be generous when selecting the motor size. However, if the calculated stress in the chain equals or is close to the permissible pull shown in Table 9–1, the choice of motor size needs careful consideration. Any available power greater

Table 9–1. Overhead trolley conveyor design factors.

Chain No.	Ultimate Strength – Pounds	Allowable Chain Pull – Pounds Roller Turn Radius – Inches						Maximum Pull – Monoplane	Minimum Radius Vertical Curve – Feet Trolley Spacing – Inches								
		18"	24"	30"	36"	42"	48" up		8"	12"	16"	18"	24"	30"	32"	36"	40"
348	24,000	600	800	1,000	1,200	1,300	1,500	2,000	–	4	–	6	8	10	–	12	–
458	48,000	1,400	1,600	1,800	2,100	2,500	3,000	4,000	6	–	8	–	10	–	12	–	16
468	70,000	–	2,000	2,500	3,000	3,600	4,000	5,000	6	–	8	–	10	–	12	–	16
658	48,000	–	–	–	2,100	2,500	3,000	4,000	–	12	–	–	15	–	–	20	–
678	85,000	–	–	–	4,000	4,500	5,000	6,000	–	12	–	–	15	–	–	20	–

Monoplane service – conveyor operates in horizontal plane only.

than the calculated horsepower can result in overloading the chain. If the calculated live load stresses the chain to its maximum allowable limit and occurs on occasion only, it would be best to use a smaller motor having high slip characteristics. For example, if the occasional heavy load indicates a 2.5-HP motor, after due allowance for drive efficiency, it is best to use a 2-HP high-slip motor. Such a motor should give satisfactory service under overload conditions for short periods of, say, one hour's duration. A 3-HP motor would permit a 20 per cent overload in the chain and continued overloading will cause chain failure. The controls on the smaller motor will shut off the power if overloading continues.

If the live load condition is continuous and the calculated chain pull equals the allowable pull, any oversize motor will permit loading the chain beyond the limit. In this case, corrective measures such as larger chain or the use of multiple drives will insure against overloading.

Table 9–2. Factors used in determining chain pull on overhead trolley conveyors.

Friction Factors*												
Rolling Friction Trolleys			Additions for Horizontal Turns						Additions for Vertical Curve			
Chain Pitch			Traction Wheel			Roller Turn			Angle			
3"	4"	6"	45°	90°	180°	45°	90°	180°	20°	30°	45°	60°
2%	1.5%	1.5%	2%	3%	5%	2.5%	4.5%	6%	3%	4%	5%	6%

*Factors should be increased if conveyor operates in dusty atmosphere or through ovens, degreasers, washers, etc.

In a simple system with few minor vertical rises and dips, relatively few horizontal turns, and a well-balanced live load, it is satisfactory to arrive at the chain pull by using the following overall friction factors. Multiply the total load to be moved (chain, trolleys, carriers, and live load) by 3 per cent friction for conveyors using the 3"-pitch chain and by 2½ per cent friction for those using 4"- or 6"-pitch chains. The weight of chain is shown in the detail table in Fig. 9–2. A two-wheel trolley will weigh 7, 8, and 12 pounds for the 3", 4", and 6" sizes, respectively.

When a system has many horizontal turns and high rises, and/or is heavily loaded, the chain pull should be calculated progressively as discussed in Chapter 8 for crossbar conveyors. The rolling friction factors and the percentage to be added for horizontal turns and vertical curves are shown in Table 9–2. The rolling friction shown is less than the overall friction factors given above for simple systems. The percentage additions given for vertical curves are in addition to the plus values added for elevating the load or the minus values credited to the pull if declines are loaded.

The pull in the chain imposes a load on the trolleys as they negotiate vertical curves. The resulting load from the chain pull plus the live load (carrier and contents) must not exceed the capacity of the trolley. The trolley wheel and bearing have great capacity but the load limits given below are the maximum that the track will support. As will be seen in

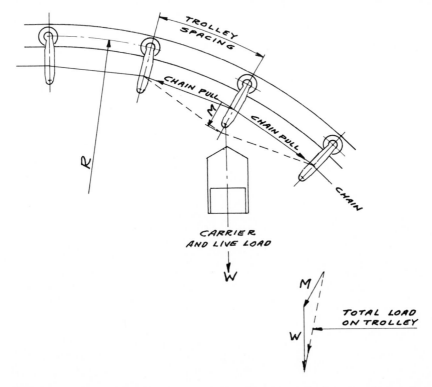

Fig. 9–3. Stress diagram for trolley loading at vertical curves in overhead trolley conveyors.

the diagram in Fig. 9–3, trolley spacing has a direct bearing on the magnitude of the load imposed on the trolley by the stress in the chain. Trolley load capacities are:

Trolley for 3″ system—400#
Trolley for 4″ system—800#
Trolley for 6″ system—1,600#

If the loading exceeds the capacity of a single trolley, load bars may be employed as shown in Fig. 9–4 to distribute the load to two or four trolleys. Load bars are sometimes used to hold the suspended load away from the chain on steep inclines rather than because of the magnitude of the load.

The standard trolley wheel has a one-piece tread that is machined to provide smooth travel. The tread is the outer race of a ball bearing with

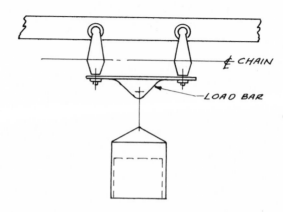

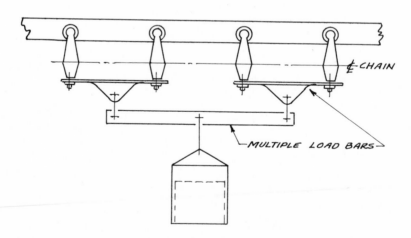

Fig. 9–4. Multiple trolley arrangements.

large balls spaced by a separator. The ball races are ground. The bearing fit is "loose" to prevent binding when subjected to changes in temperature and to permit freer action in dusty atmospheres. Other types of wheels are available for trolleys, such as pressed steel two-piece races, unground races, etc. The various modifications result in lower costs of trolleys but they are limited in service by load-carrying capacity or by their ability to operate only under specific favorable conditions.

Drop

The distance from the center line of the suspended chain to the I-beam track is known as the "drop." This dimension varies with different manufacturers, but the majority of makes have a common figure for each of the several sizes. The overhead trolley conveyor can readily be changed to alter the path of travel. In making such changes in existing systems, it is important that any new trolleys be purchased from the original vendor or one who can furnish trolleys with the same drop. In many installations it is equally important that the distance from the chain center line to the load attachment hole be uniform. This is especially critical if there are automatic loading or unloading stations in the system.

Carriers

The carriers, trays, or cars take many forms. Some of the more common types are shown in Fig. 9–5. With the hook, tree, or open carrier, the load supporting member(s) is shaped to accommodate the product being handled. With the open carrier or any of the three closed carriers shown, the load may be a package, a container, a bale or a roll of paper, wire or metal strip, etc. The shape and type of carrier bed vary with the kind of load. Where the carrier is mounted directly to two trolleys, the top member of the carrier acts as a load bar. With this construction the conveyor usually operates in the horizontal plane only. The carrier will tip on inclines, but under favorable conditions this may be permissible.

In a load bar or other connection between trolleys, the hole for the second or following attachment must be slotted to permit movement of this connecting bolt. As the conveyor negotiates turns, the chord between trolleys is shorter than the trolley spacing.

On all but the tree carrier, loads can be automatically loaded and/or unloaded. The hook carrier can pick up a load as it advances. To unload, the load may be retarded and the hook pulled out as the conveyor advances.

On the other carriers, open or closed, the bed of the carrier may be equipped with rollers to permit manual or automatic load and unload without lifting the product. The bottoms of the carriers can be arranged to tilt at designated points to discharge their contents. Tilting beds are common for rolling round loads off at discharge points.

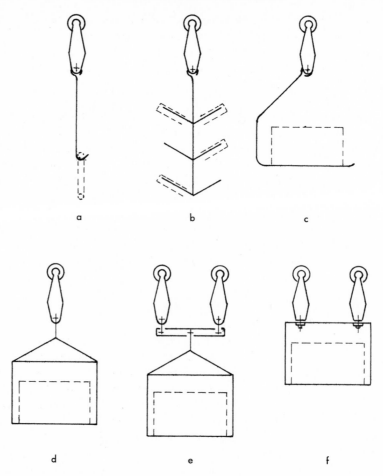

Fig. 9–5. Overhead trolley conveyor carriers. (a) Hook carrier. (b) Tree carrier. (c) Open carrier. *Closed carriers:* (d) Single trolley. (e) Load bar. (f) Mounted to trolley.

LOADING AND UNLOADING

The bottoms of the carriers can be arranged with fingers to permit alternate fingers on a loading or unloading station to place the product into or remove it from the traveling carrier. Some typical stations are illustrated in Fig. 9–6.

The arrangement in Fig. 9–6(a) shows an open-bottom carrier supporting a container or other unit on two side ledges of the carrier. As the carrier enters the unloading zone, a cam guide holds the carrier steady as it travels through the station. When the carrier is directly above the lift, the bed of the lift is elevated and raises the container off the carrier ledges. After the carrier has moved on, the lift lowers the container to the level of the takeaway conveyor. The same mechanism can be used to load the carrier. The container is raised above the level of the ledges on the carrier before it (the carrier) enters the loading zone. When the carrier is fully under the container, the lift drops and deposits the container into the carrier.

Figure 9–6(b) shows another means of unloading an open-bottom carrier. Here the carrier passes over the takeaway conveyor, depositing its container or other unit load as it advances. The bottom of the carrier could consist of several fingers in place of the open construction. That

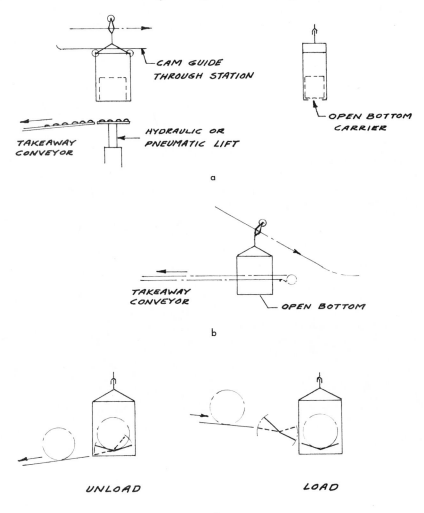

Fig. 9–6. Loading and unloading stations for trolley conveyor.

portion of the takeaway conveyor under the carrier's path is then equipped with alternating fingers mounting narrow rollers or wheels. The container rolls out on these fingers as the carrier deposits it. Loading of the carrier can be accomplished in a similar manner. A conveyor would bring the container to a loading station where the container would come to rest. The carrier then combs up, around, or through the station, picking up the load.

In Fig. 9–6(c) a carrier with a rounded bed conveys a circular load. As it reaches the unloading point, the bed of the carrier is tilted and the round load rolls out onto skids or another type of takeaway conveyor. When being loaded, the round load comes to rest in a loading station adjacent to the path of the carriers on the conveyor. When an empty carrier is in a proper position, the loading station bed tilts and the load rolls onto the bed of the carrier.

Any pendant carrier can be made to rotate to any degree or continuously as it advances. A disc or gear is mounted on the pendant close to the attachment at the trolley or load bar. The disc or gear contacts a friction bar or gear rack as the carrier is advanced.

SUSPENSION METHODS

There are many means of connecting the carrier to the trolley. The most common are the clevis type and the rod type. These are shown in

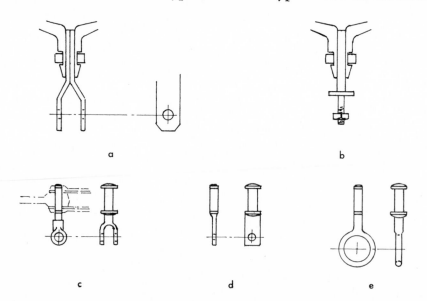

Fig. 9–7. Chain attachments. (a) Clevis attachment. (b) Rod attachment. *Chain pin attachments:* (c) Clevis type. (d) I-type. (e) Ring type.

Fig. 9–7. Also illustrated are some of the more popular extended pin attachments. The latter are used to support very light loads at points between trolleys.

Engineering

HORIZONTAL TURNS

Horizontal turns are of three general types: sprocket wheels, roller turns, and traction wheels.

Sprocket wheel turns are usually confined to use at corner drives. This type of drive is necessarily restricted to use on conveyors handling very small loads that can successfully negotiate the small radius of the corner. Long loads or loads requiring load bars will not clear if the radius is too small. Large diameter sprockets are difficult to mount and they can readily result in excessive torque at the drive shaft.

Roller turns consist of closely spaced heavy-duty ball-bearing rollers mounted in a formed frame. Figure 9–8 shows the relation of the turn to the I-beam track, chain, and trolley. As the chain articulates in the horizontal plane, the roller turn can be made with small radii if the load

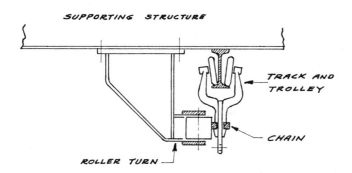

Fig. 9–8. Roller turn for trolley conveyor.

size and the pull in the chain permit. Turns larger than the 48″ radius indicated in Table 9–1 are available. Standard angle turns are 15°, 30°, 45°, 60°, 90°, and 180°. The radius or the angle of the turn can be other than standard to meet special requirements. The roller turn can be used at wall openings, building columns, etc., where sprocket or traction wheel turns would not be practical.

Traction wheel turns are made with flat face wheels that revolve normally on bronze bushings in the hubs. Ball bearings in the hub of the wheel can be obtained. The traction wheel is used chiefly in ovens, washers, degreasers, sandblast enclosures, etc., where it is desirable to reduce lubrication and maintenance to a minimum.

On any type of horizontal turn it is important to have perfect alignment of the sprocket, wheel, or rollers with the I-beam track to keep the trolleys properly centered on the track.

VERTICAL CURVES

Vertical curves are used at changes in elevation of the conveyor. A curve is the complete compound track segment shown in Fig. 9–9. The

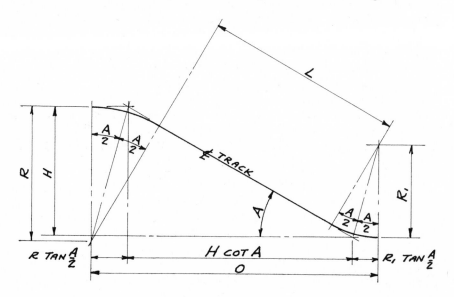

Fig. 9–9. Vertical curve design for trolley conveyor track.

radius R at the upper curve must be the minimum shown in Table 9–1 for a given trolley spacing. The radius R_1 at the lower curve can be somewhat smaller than R if necessary but in most installations is the same as R. As shown previously, the load imposed in the trolley due to stress in the chain at the upper curve is added to the total carrier and live load on the trolley. At the lower curve, however, the load imposed by the chain pull lifts the trolley against the upper flange of the I-beam track. The load of carrier and live load is acting in an opposing direction and the net load is less, resulting in less load on the flanges of the track. Also, the chain pull at the lower curve is less than the pull at the upper curve. This difference is appreciable when length of straight track between curves or distance L is great.

The overall length O of the compound curve, when L is zero, is:

$$\sin A \ (R \text{ plus } R_1)$$

When a straight section of track length L is used between the curves, the overall length O becomes:

$$H \cot A \text{ plus } \tan A/2 \ (R \text{ plus } R_1)$$

The angle of incline should be kept to a minimum, and the radii of the curves should be as large as possible for the best results. In many layouts, however, floor space is at a premium; it is then necessary to use minimal radii and maximal angles of inclines. Heavy live loads on the trolleys tend to cant them as they negotiate the inclines. Angles generally should be no greater than 45°, and many engineers limit the angle to 30°. Steeper angles can be used—a few installations have even been made with vertical runs—but all operating factors must be considered, and steep angles should be used only under very favorable conditions.

DRIVES

Drives for overhead conveyors are of two general types: the corner sprocket drive and the caterpillar drive.

Most standard corner drives use a 36″ pitch diameter sprocket. It is usually applied at a 90° or a 180° turn. Since the radius is small, the drive is limited in use by the size of the load being handled.

The caterpillar drive uses a short loop of auxiliary chain running parallel to the main conveyor chain. The auxiliary chain is equipped with driving dogs that engage the main chain. Back-up bars on the auxiliary chain and rollers on the main chain side keep the driving dogs properly engaged. Figure 9–10 shows the general arrangement of the caterpillar drive. The drive sprocket can be small, making the torque requirements low and usually producing an economical drive especially on the heavier-duty conveyors. The caterpillar drive is also more versatile, for it can be placed at any point where the chain pull approaches the maximum recommended. The drive also permits the use of large-radius roller turns for all horizontal corners, and this is particularly important when large and/or closely spaced loads are being handled.

As is true of all chain conveyor drives, provision should be made for a mechanical overload device to avoid damage in event of a jam. Unlike belt or belt driven conveyors, where the belting can slip on the drive pulley in the event of a sudden massive overload, the conveying chain is positively geared to the driving medium.

A mechanical overload device should provide protection at any speed. In constant-speed drives, the device can be located at almost any point in the driving machine. In a variable-speed drive, however, the overload device cannot be located at the motor end as very little protection will then be provided at the slower speeds.

A shear pin sprocket, in which the sprocket half is free to turn on the drive shaft and the hub is keyed to the shaft, will provide economical protection. The shear pin, however, does not usually shut off power to the motor. Another objection that many designers have is the tendency to replace a sheared pin with one having a higher shear value, thus losing the needed protection.

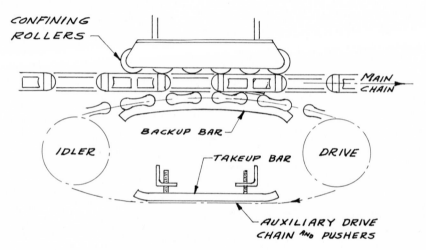

Fig. 9–10. Caterpillar chain drive.

Some manufacturers mount the entire drive on a sliding base. The driving effort is resisted by compression springs. If an overload occurs, the sliding base is forced back against the springs and contacts a limit switch cutting off power to the motor. The location of the limit switch can be adjusted to operate only when a predetermined limit in the chain pull occurs.

Constant-speed drives usually employ a V-belt drive from the motor to the high-speed shaft of a vertical gear reducer. The output or slow-speed shaft of the reducer may mount the sprocket of a corner sprocket drive or the drive sprocket on a caterpillar drive.

Variable-speed drives use the simple varipulley for all speed variations up to about 3:1. For greater variations in speed the more elaborate variable-speed transmissions are used.

Multiple constant-speed or variable-speed drives can be used on long and/or heavily loaded conveyors. A drive should be placed wherever the pull in the chain reaches the allowable limit for the chain. There is no theoretical limit to the number of drives that can be used on one conveyor. There are, however, problems in matching drive speeds so that the driving effort is distributed properly to the various motors. The number of drives that can be used is an economic consideration. Many drives can be synchronized if the cost of controls can be justified. Probably more drives can be used on a constant-speed conveyor than would be economically practical on a variable-speed conveyor.

Earlier in this chapter a hypothetical case indicated that a 2.5-HP motor was required. If the pull in the chain remained constant at the permissible limit, it was suggested that multiple drives would be one solution to the problem. One drive could be 1.5 HP, while a second drive could be equipped with a 1-HP motor.

When constant-speed multiple drives are used, high-slip motors should be specified. The horsepower of each motor must be carefully calculated (all motors need not be the same power). As an overload occurs at one drive due to heavy loading or tight chain, the motor will slow down. It will turn again at normal speed as soon as the heavy loading passes to the next drive, or when the chain has loosened due to the slowdown operation while the other drive(s) was operating at full speed. In the use of multiple drives, best results will be obtained if the chain is not stressed too highly. If more than five drives are used it is considered best to limit the chain pull to about 60 per cent of the allowable pulls shown in Table 9-1.

In multiple-drive conveyors, the various strands of chain, even if equal in footage, do not necessarily have the same number of chain pitches. The length of chain passing each drive must be equal in lineal feet. The drives, having sprockets with the same number of teeth, will advance equal number of pitches every revolution. Therefore, the drives must be able to operate at different speeds to keep the system operating smoothly.

If the conveyor has variable speed, the matching of multiple drives becomes more complicated. It is possible that, if only two drives are involved, the speed can be varied manually; in most cases, however, electrical control with the use of direct current motors will prove best. Such electrical control is necessary if more than two drives are involved. A sophisticated control system is a necessity if the live load varies greatly in the length of the conveyor and/or if the loading is heavy.

Whether the conveyor has one drive or multiple drives, the location of each drive is important. In multiple-drive systems the location of drives can be arranged to aid materially in reducing the synchronizing problem. Extreme care is necessary in working out the loading in the chain. As mentioned before, a drive is placed at or before the point in the system where the allowable limit of chain pull is reached. Also, the drive must be located at the top of or after a vertical rise. If it can be located just before the conveyor starts down a decline, the natural pull down may be sufficient to keep the chain tight as it exits from the drive. If the decline or natural takeup is not available, a mechanical takeup must be provided. Drives should not be located just before the rise in a vertical curve because the slack chain, leaving the drive, will bunch, and jams will result. For the same reason, drives should not be placed where there is a long stretch of horizontal track ahead. A takeup is necessary to absorb the slack chain, and the takeup must be located at a turn.

TAKEUPS

Takeups should be provided on all overhead trolley conveyors. It may be a manually operated screw takeup or an automatic type actuated by springs, counterweights, or pneumatic or hydraulic cylinders. In most installations the takeup need only be long enough to permit removal of two pitches of chain. If the conveyor uses automatic loading or unloading stations, or if for any other reason the spacing between carriers must be maintained, the takeup adjustment must be long enough to allow removal of a complete carrier spacing.

Springs may be used for automatically maintaining chain tension on the short takeups, for they are usually less than 9″ in length of adjustment. On longer adjustments the use of counterweights or hydraulic and pneumatic cylinders is more satisfactory because the pull in the takeup mechanism is constant throughout its travel.

Power-and-Free Systems

Power-and-free conveyor systems are used extensively where it is desired to combine trolley conveyors with machine tools and other equipment to form an integrated system of automatic handling. They are used where loads must be temporarily stored or stopped for manufacturing operations and/or inspection. The power-and-free system satisfies any condition that would not permit continuous movement at a fixed speed or spacing, a feature of a regular overhead trolley conveyor.

The power is supplied by a conventional trolley conveyor; the load-supporting trolleys operate over a separate track. In some arrangements the power line is located alongside the free line, and pusher dogs engage projecting arms on the free trolleys. In other designs the power line is directly above the free line. This latter arrangement is used when it is desired to divert the free load-carrying trolleys to both sides of the main line.

The free trolleys may be shunted onto a side track where they can accumulate or be re-engaged by another power unit to convey them at a different speed and/or at a spacing other than that provided by the main power line. After the necessary operations have been performed, or when the stored loads are again required, the free trolleys may be automatically fed back into the main system.

Many accessories such as switches, turntables, and elevating and lowering units are all available to control the movement of the free trolleys through sophisticated handling systems. The ability to dispatch loads automatically and to transfer them readily justifies the higher cost of the power-and-free systems in many operations.

10

Tow Conveyors

Tow conveyors are employed to transport four-wheel trucks over a fixed path. Curves and ramps or inclines can be readily negotiated.

Chains of the type described in Chapter 9 are used on tow conveyors. The chain may be suspended from trolleys operating on an overhead track, and in all respects the conveyor is similar to the overhead trolley conveyor. In this overhead type of tow conveyor the trucks are equipped with slings that engage hook attachments suspended from the trolleys, or the truck may be fitted with a rigid mast that can be raised to engage the hook attachments. Figure 10–1 shows both of these methods of engaging the trucks to the conveyor.

In the other type of tow conveyor, the chain is installed below the floor line. A simple tow pin is located in the front center of the truck. This pin is dropped through a slot in the floor, to be engaged by pusher attachments on the chain. A detail of this construction is shown in Fig. 10–2.

As mentioned in Chapter 3, there are economical and physical factors that determine whether an overhead or an "in-the-floor" type of tow conveyor should be used.

Load Calculation

In either type of conveyor, the load imposed on the chain attachment can be calculated by allowing 2 per cent friction for the movement of the truck. This friction is based on trucks having anti-friction bearing wheels, and smooth, level floors having a hard surface that will not be gouged or channeled by the trucks' wheels. If the wheels are less than 6″ in diameter, if wheel bearings are worn, or if the floor is in poor condition, it will be necessary to increase the friction factor. Generally these poor operating conditions tend to worsen, and it is recommended that the trucks and the floor be reconditioned rather than using a higher friction

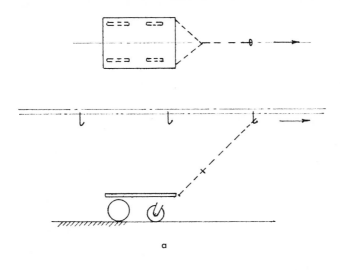

a

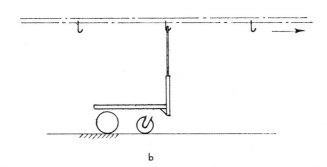

b

Fig. 10–1. Overhead tow conveyor. (a) Sling attachment. (b) Rigid mast attachment.

factor that may prove inadequate after the conveyor is in operation for a period of time. A simple draw-bar test will determine the proper friction, if there is any reason to question the proper figure for the truck being considered.

In most installations a filled truck is engaged to the conveyor while the truck is still moving. Therefore, the additional friction required to start the truck from rest is not a factor. If an occasional truck is started from rest and/or there are only one or two loading points for filled trucks, the additional starting friction can be ignored. However, if there are many loading points and there is a possibility that several trucks will be en-

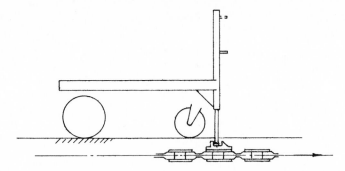

Fig. 10–2. In-the-floor tow conveyor.

gaged by the conveyor simultaneously, the additional starting load on the chain should be calculated.

If ramps are to be negotiated, the additional chain pull must be calculated to lift the load up the rise. No allowance should be made for declines.

Speed

Conveyor speeds up to 60 FPM are common. Greater speeds are possible but some objectionable features will probably then be involved. Cross traffic is common along the path of the conveyor line, but becomes hazardous at high speeds. Trucks tend to whip around curves and, with the overhead type especially, the trucks can tip over at high speeds. Loads on the trucks can be dislodged at curves. At higher speeds the "bumping" of trucks at discharge points can also dislodge loads and in some cases damage the trucks. In some operations the higher speeds can prove troublesome, especially if trucks start from rest. Speeds greater than 60 FPM should therefore be used only after consideration of all factors.

Automatic Diversion and Discharge

As mentioned in Chapter 3, varied means are available for coding the destination of the truck when automatic diversion is required. (A more complete discussion of the different means is included in Chapter 16.)

At the automatic discharge points, it is generally required that several trucks be permitted to accumulate. The momentum of the trucks will vary. The variation in the weight of the filled truck is the chief factor affecting the travel distance of the disengaged truck. Some trucks will coast completely clear of the path of the main conveyor line. Others may stop with the back end still in the path, and these will be "bumped" out of the way by the next passing truck or by another truck entering the same discharge point.

A slot in the floor at the discharge point keeps the trucks in line. In most instances the maximum number of trucks that can be accumulated should be limited to three or four.

When a large number of trucks must be accumulated, there are two methods that have been employed successfully. One method is to decline the floor at the discharge spur about ⅛″ per foot. This increases the distance a truck will roll and reduces the force required to advance previously discharged trucks when the next truck enters the spur. This arrangement, however, may not be practical in all building constructions. Also, the slight grade may prove to be too much for a truck with the maximum load and with good bearings in the wheels.

A more positive method is to equip the spur with an indexing conveyor in the floor. This conveyor is equipped with dogs or attachments that engage the tow pin of the discharged truck and advance it slightly more than one truck length. As a truck enters the spur, the conveyor is activated and advances the new as well as all the previously accumulated trucks. In this way the trucks are under control at all times and they do not bump into each other. The number of trucks that can accumulate in this type of discharge station is limited only by the length of the spur line and the indexing conveyor.

The overhead type of tow conveyor may employ any of the chains shown for overhead trolley conveyors in Chapter 9. The conveyor may be calculated in the same manner as are trolley conveyors, by substituting the load imposed by the truck in place of the suspended load on the trolley conveyor. Most overhead tow conveyors use the no. 458 chain.

The floor-type tow conveyor, because of the pusher and idler attachments on the chain, uses the no. 658 chain. In calculating the chain pull on this type, use the following formula:

Feet of assembled chain in the conveyor loop	@ 5.5#/ft.	. . . . . .
Number of loaded trucks	@ lbs.	. . . . . .
Number of empty trucks	@ lbs.	. . . . . .
Total moving load		. . . . . .

Multiply this total load by 2 per cent to arrive at the chain pull.

The use of multiple drives, when necessary, is treated in the same manner as described in Chapter 9 for overhead trolley conveyors.

Many installations require a series of tow conveyor loops. There may be several conveyors located on the same floor level or they may be located on separate floors. Automatic transfer of trucks from one conveyor to another is possible. If the conveyor loops are located on the same floor, a truck is automatically diverted at a transfer line. Here the trucks accumulate and await an empty pusher attachment on the conveyor they are to enter. The transfer line is powered with a separate conveyor that accepts the trucks from one conveyor and feeds them, when a space is available, to the other conveyor.

If the conveyors are located on different floor levels, the transfer line incorporates a vertical conveyor that raises or lowers the truck to the desired level.

Assume three tow conveyors in a system: #1, #2, and #3. If conveyor #1 has ten diverting points, they are numbered 1–1 to 1–10. If conveyor #2 has eight diverting points, they are numbered 2–1 to 2–8; if conveyor #3 has thirty diverting points, they are numbered 3–1 to 3–30. A truck may be engaged at any point on any of the three conveyors, to be diverted at any of the forty-eight diverting points. Complete intercommunication is possible. The complexity of the control equipment necessary to maintain the destination code through the transfer from one conveyor to another depends on the type of coding employed.

Automatic disengagement of the truck from the tow line is accomplished in several ways. An electromechanical device has been used to disengage trucks from the overhead type of tow conveyor. The rigid mast attachment on the truck is used for this purpose.

The floor-type tow conveyor is more adaptable to automatic deflection or diversion. A mechanical device consisting of an auxiliary pin, in addition to the main tow pin, is used. This auxiliary pin can be set at various locations across the front of the truck indicating its prescribed destination. When the truck arrives at the location having a secondary slot in the floor in alignment with the auxiliary pin, the pin drops into the slot and the truck is moved from the main line and moves into the side spur.

Various electronic systems can be used for coding the trucks to a specific spur line destination. In designs using these systems, a switch plate is caused to swing across the main line slot just ahead of the tow pin on the truck to be diverted. The switch forces the truck into the spur line slot and after the tow pin has passed, the switch plate returns to the open position clearing the main line slot again.

Multiplane Systems

As mentioned above, the overhead type of tow conveyor utilizes a regular overhead trolley conveyor, as described in Chapter 9. In a level or monoplane system, either the sling attachment or the rigid mast attachment can be used. In a system involving ramps (a multiplane system), it is best to use the "in-the-floor" type. However, the rigid mast attachment

Fig. 10–3. Overhead trolley tow conveyor. (Courtesy Alvey-Ferguson Company.)

can be used with an overhead-type conveyor if the ramps are gradual so that the truck does not "run away" on the declines.

The floor-type conveyor, while using the same type of chain and employing roller turns to guide the chain around curves, does differ from the overhead trolley conveyor in construction. Figure 10–4 shows a typical cross section through the conveyor. Pits are provided for the

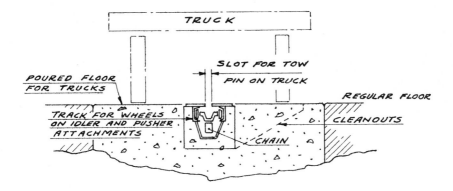

Fig. 10–4. Detail (section) of construction of floor tow conveyor, showing idler attachment.

caterpillar drive(s); enlarged troughs are provided for the curves, and clean-out areas are provided every 200' to 300' to permit removal of debris that may drop through the slot in the floor.

The pusher attachments are provided with latches that confine the tow pin of the truck; this type of tow conveyor is therefore ideal for multiplane applications.

11

Vertical Conveyors

Vertical conveyors take many forms. They may be manually or automatically loaded and/or unloaded. They can automatically connect conveyor systems serving several levels. They are designed to handle any type of load.

The simple dumbwaiter, when manually loaded and unloaded, is not normally considered a "conveyor." Such equipment is usually classified in the same grouping with freight and passenger elevators.

Vertical Reciprocating Conveyors

The vertical conveyor that consists of a car traveling up and down in guides is known as a vertical reciprocating conveyor. The car is of a design that accommodates the particular unit load being handled. This conveyor never conveys people.

The car may consist of a bed of roller conveyor, live-roll conveyor, belt conveyor, or any form of chain conveyor. Cartons, boxes, pallets, drums, barrels, rolled material on end, or any type of container can be accommodated by the specially designed car bed. The bed of the car may consist of formed members to cradle any round object such as drums, barrels, rolls of metal, paper, etc. Figure 11–1 shows several typical designs of cars used.

The drive for the vertical reciprocating conveyor may include a winding drum or it may consist of a driven sheave or sprocket if the car is counterweighted. Figure 11–2 shows the various types of drives most commonly used.

Cable is generally preferred over chain in the counterweighted drive because of its flexibility and the ease with which multiple strands may be applied for safety, when heavy loads are being handled.

The magnitude of the counterweight should be equal to the weight of the complete car plus one-half the weight of the load. The weight of the unbalanced load on the drive machinery is then the same for a full or empty car.

The car and the counterweight are usually equipped with sliding shoes that ride on steel guide members. These shoes are frequently lined with

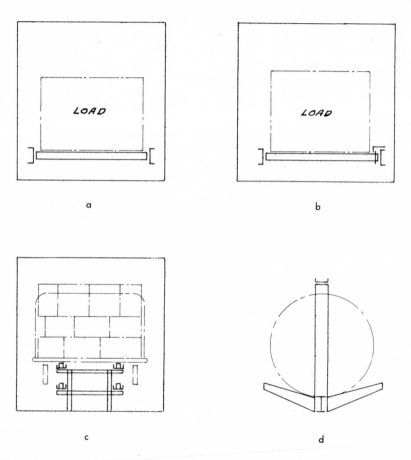

Fig. 11–1. Cars for vertical reciprocating conveyors. (a) Roller bed for flat-bottom loads. (b) Powered bed for flat-bottom loads (driven rolls shown). (c) Chain conveyor bed (truck load shown). (d) Cradle bed for round loads.

replaceable friction-resisting material. If the load in the car causes an unbalanced condition on the car guides, it may be advisable to use rollers or wheels in the car shoes to reduce friction.

The net load to be raised or lowered, when multiplied by the speed, will indicate the power required at the drive drum, sheave, or sprocket. An additional 10 per cent is normally calculated to compensate for friction of the car and counterweight in the guides. If the live load in the car causes a severe imbalance and/or the conveyor is designed for heavy duty, it is best to calculate the exact friction for each element.

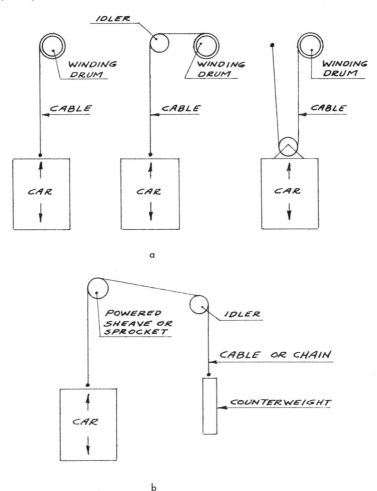

Fig. 11–2. Arrangements of vertical reciprocating conveyors. (a) Drum-type drives. (b) Counterweighted car.

The capacity of the vertical reciprocating conveyor is low—one or two round trips per minute—and the speed of travel is slow. The impact of the car entering the upper or lower stations can then be absorbed or cushioned with pliable pads or with springs. Slight variations in landing elevations can usually be tolerated, especially if the car bed and the station conveyors are powered.

At high speeds or where exact leveling is essential, a two-speed motor is recommended so that the car enters the terminals at slow speed. Leveling controls may be required under some conditions.

On occasion, an intermediate station(s) must be served. Dynamic braking or leveling controls have been used to assure proper registration with upper, lower, and intermediate station conveyors.

SPEED

The vertical conveyor should never be operated faster than necessary to provide the capacity required. Assume a conveyor travel of 12'–0". The load is 3'–0" long, and the horizontal conveyors in the car and stations operate at 40 FPM. Capacity required is one (1) load per minute. Assume further that the live load will travel 4'–0" to clear the loading station and that the car conveyor is 4'–0" long. The speed required on this vertical is then:

Loading operation: 8' travel @ 40 FPM   = 12 seconds
Allowance to close electrical contacts   = 1 second
Unloading operation: 4' travel @ 40 FPM = 6 seconds
Allowance to close electrical contacts   = 1 second
                                       20 seconds

Time available for 2 trips @ 12'   = 40 seconds

$$\text{Speed required} = \frac{24 \times 60}{40} = 36 \text{ FPM}$$

An actual speed of 40 FPM would be planned to assure the required capacity of one load or one complete circuit of the car every minute.

Speeds in excess of 60 FPM and/or loads exceeding 500 pounds usually will require special treatment (two-speed motors, dynamic braking, etc.) to allow the car to register smoothly at the stations.

LOADING AND UNLOADING

If roller gravity conveyors are used in the car and in the loading and unloading stations, the time to load and unload cannot be calculated as accurately as when the horizontal conveyors are powered. The grade used and the nature of the load bottom will affect the speed of the load starting from rest. Normally, an average speed of 30 FPM will give a good indication of the time needed to start a load and have it travel the distance of a little over its own length.

The automatic loading station of the vertical is arranged to permit only one load to enter the car. When the loading conveyor is roller gravity, a simple escapement device may be sufficient to hold back other loads while one load is entering the car. If the space between load bottoms is not available for the use of the escapement, two hinged sections of roller conveyor can be used. These two common devices are shown in Fig. 11–3.

In many designs, the escapement or hinged sections are actuated by the motion of the car entering the loading station. Therefore, if no load is in the escapement area or on the hinged section, none can enter after the car has arrived at the station. For this reason the operation requires that the car remain at the unloading station until a load does enter the loading station. The load contacts an electrical switch and "calls" the car.

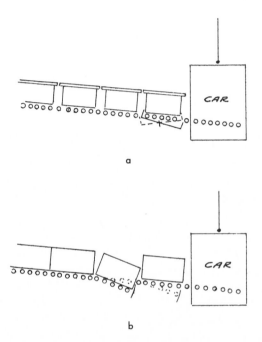

Fig. 11–3. Loading stations for vertical reciprocating conveyors. (a) Escapement-type load station. (b) Hinged load station.

When the loading station consists of powered conveyors, the start and stop operations of the loading conveyor insure that only one unit will enter the vertical. A typical station of this type is illustrated in Fig. 11–4. Any form of power conveyor can be used. When the loading conveyor is operating, the feeding conveyor stops and holds back the other waiting units. The feeding conveyor is also arranged to stop when a unit arrives at the proper position on the loading conveyor. This latter conveyor operates at a greater speed than the feeding conveyor to assure separation of the unit to be loaded from the others on the feeding conveyor.

With a powered loading station, the position of the car in the vertical at the time the load arrives at the station is immaterial. The car may be at the loading level; if so, the loading conveyor continues to operate until the unit is completely positioned on the car. The feeding conveyor does not start operating until the loading conveyor is empty and ready to receive another unit.

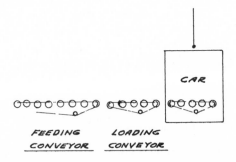

Fig. 11–4. Powered loading stations for vertical reciprocating conveyors.

Modifications of the powered loading station are used. The feeding conveyor may be replaced with a series of short conveyors, each slightly longer than the length of the unit load. The series of conveyors are electrically interlocked so that any conveyor operates only when the conveyor ahead is empty and ready to receive a load. Such an arrangement is also used when it is essential to keep the units from contacting each other.

In all of the automatic stations described above, the unit loads are of equal or nearly equal length. Any great variation in length would require special treatment, and in most such cases the vertical reciprocating conveyor would prove to be more costly than some other form of conveyor.

MODIFIED SYSTEMS

There are many variations of the vertical reciprocating conveyor principle. Installations have been made so that the car will accommodate two or more loads. This has been done to achieve greater capacity. However, the need to wait at times for a full complement of loads to enter the car defeats the prime purpose of doubling, tripling, etc., the capacity. Also, the more complicated and expensive electrical controls may make the installation of two single-duty conveyors more practical and possibly more economical.

Other installations have been made using two cars. The second car replaces the counterweight of the standard conveyor. Here again, the need to interlock two loading and two unloading stations will entail some lost time in waiting for all stations to clear before the cars can start the vertical travel. Such an arrangement may prove to be more practical than the multiple-load car design described above, but the initial and operating costs should be carefully compared with those of two standard units. This two-car design is sometimes used to provide two-way service, i.e., for raising and lowering loads. However, if two-way service is the only requirement, the more economical modification described below may be advisable.

A common modification of the vertical reciprocating conveyor is to utilize the unit for up and down service simultaneously. At each level, the vertical is equipped with a loading station on one side and an unloading station on the opposite side. Powered conveyors in the stations and in the car are desirable. The car arriving at one level will discharge its load and immediately receive another load from the loading station, if there is one waiting to enter the car. With comparatively simple electrical control, two-way service can be obtained.

Two-way service is also possible on a single standard unit by using reversible powered conveyors in the stations and the car. Obviously, this vertical can be used for only one service at any given time. The loading station in one direction of travel becomes the unloading station when the conveyor is used for the reverse service.

Gravity-operated Verticals

Another form of vertical reciprocating conveyor is operated by the force of gravity. In this design, the counterweight is enclosed in a sealed tube. The counterweight is heavier than the car so that the car is always raised to the upper level. When a load is deposited on the car, the overbalance causes the loaded car to drop. An air cushion in the tube arrests the high-speed travel of the counterweight and cushions the loaded car to a stop at the lower level or unloading station. When the load has discharged from the car, the heavier counterweight drops in the tube and the car is raised again to the upper or loading level. The air cushion at the bottom of the tube arrests the fall of the counterweight and eases the car into the upper station. High-speed operation is possible and automatic loading and unloading are available, but loads must be uniform in weight.

The gravity-operated vertical is frequently used in handling stereotype plates in the printing industry. The plates leave the shavers, enter the "drops," and are rapidly lowered to the press-room level. Simple mechanical stops effect automatic loading while the plates travel over graded wheel or roller conveyors. At the lower discharge point, a "kicker" is actuated when the car enters the station, and the plate is quickly ejected from the car.

The use of this gravity-operated unit is not confined to handling comparatively light loads such as the stereotype plates mentioned. Heavy loads also can be conveyed with this unit. The only requirement is that the weight of the loads be reasonably uniform.

Suspended-tray Conveyors

When greater capacities are required, the vertical suspended-tray conveyor is used. This conveyor consists of endless chains running continuously over top and bottom sprockets. A series of cars is suspended from the chains. There are two major forms of this conveyor—the "center suspended" and the "corner suspended" types. These units are illustrated in Fig. 11–5.

The cars on the vertical suspended-tray conveyor are constructed with spaced "fingers" to facilitate loading and unloading operations while the cars are moving. The cars comb through open finger construction in the loading and unloading stations. Two strands of chain operate over top and bottom pairs of sprockets. Special chain pins are extended at intervals, or special attachments on the chains are used to mount trunnion pins from which the cars are suspended. The cars negotiate the sprocket turns by pivoting on these pins. The suspension hanger is usually of sufficient length to prevent tipping of the load as the cars move over the upper sprockets. If hanger suspension is necessarily short and/or even slight, swaying or tipping cannot be tolerated; the conveyor is equipped with auxiliary guiding devices to control the level of the cars at the upper turn. Since most designs call for loading the traveling cars on the up side and unloading on the down side, leveling devices are not required around the bottom sprockets because the cars are then empty.

SPEED

Suspended-tray conveyors usually operate at speeds of 60 FPM or less. The tray or car spacing then determines the capacity of the conveyor or the number of unit loads conveyed per minute. The tendency of the cars to sway as they pass over the upper sprockets; the need to keep to a minimum the impact shock as the cars pick up the loads at the loading stations and as they deposit loads on the unloading stations; the desire to reduce wear in the chain elements at sprockets; and the need for cars to engage and disengage the car leveling device at the top, if one is used—all these dictate that the conveyor should not operate at higher speed than necessary. This general rule should be tempered somewhat if the capacity is

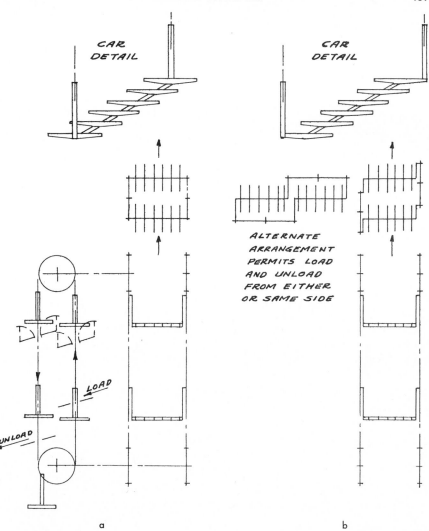

Fig. 11–5. Suspended-tray vertical conveyors. (a) Center suspension. (b) Corner suspension.

low. For example, if capacity is six loads per minute and the car spacing can be 4′–0″, the indicated speed is 24 FPM. The type of load, however, may permit operation at, say, 48 FPM and the spacing of cars increased to 8′–0″ centers. The economy of fewer cars can then be realized.

It must be remembered that loads enter the loading station between moving cars and, if the cars are spaced too closely, they may interfere with good loading operation.

If the capacity is such that high speed is indicated, it would be well to consider other means of elevating or lowering the loads. Inclined belt conveyors, pusher-bar boosters, inclined slat conveyors, etc., are all possible alternatives.

SUSPENSION AND LOAD CALCULATION

The height of the hanger should normally be such that the pivot point on the car is well above the center of gravity of the load and car bed. A suspension of about twice the center of gravity will in most cases avoid the need of a car-leveling device. The corner suspension construction has a much greater tendency to hold the cars level over the top sprockets. The direction of the twisting stresses, however, requires that the car be rugged.

A long car suspension may require unreasonably large diameter sprockets at the top, to permit the cars to clear the through shaft of the center suspension type. Stub shaft construction for these upper sprockets may then be more economical of both money and space. Stub shaft construction is required on all sprockets in the corner suspension type, regardless of hanger length.

Whenever possible, an even number of cars should be used in the conveyor to reduce the magnitude of the unbalanced load. The maximum torque or horsepower requirement at the head shaft(s) occurs when all cars on the up side are filled and all cars on the down side are empty. The total unbalanced load is then:

> Number of loads on up side @
> Impact of one live load
> Weight of one car (if an odd number)   _____
> Add 10 per cent for friction (cars in guides)   _____
>   Total unbalanced load

This unbalanced load multiplied by the chain speed will give the horsepower requirement at the head shaft.

The cars are equipped with shoes or wheels that operate in vertical guides. The chains are propelling mediums only, and therefore no rollers are required in the chains. Steel bushed-type chains or one of the combination chains are recommended. The maximum load in a single strand of chain is one half of the total load, as calculated below:

> Maximum number of cars on one side @
> Maximum number of loads on one side @
> Impact of one load
> $\frac{1}{2}$ weight of all chain
> $\frac{1}{2}$ weight of takeup or bottom shaft assembly   _____
> Add 10 per cent for friction   _____
>   Total weight on two strands of chain

LOADING AND UNLOADING

The station fingers in the vertical conveyor are normally constructed with wheels or short rollers in the fingers to facilitate movement of flat-bottom loads. If round loads are being handled, the car beds as well as the station bed are made similar to the cradle bed shown in Fig. 11–1.

The loading and unloading conveyors outside of the vertical proper are constructed similarly to those described for the vertical reciprocating

Fig. 11–6. Load and unload stations of a vertical conveyor handling trays or containers of correspondence. (Courtesy Lamson Corporation.)

conveyor. The chief difference is in the timing of release by the loading conveyor. Loads must be allowed to travel into the loading station of the continuous vertical between the moving cars. The next load cannot be released until the bottom of the previous car has cleared the station. Likewise, the unloading conveyor must operate fast enough to keep the unloading station fingers free of loads.

When more than one loading station is used and/or multiple unloading stations are incorporated in the design, all but the bottom station fingers must be hinged. Thus they can be folded out of the vertical path of the cars when not being used.

When the load being handled is unusually large and/or heavy—for example, a 4,000# pallet load—it is best to use power conveyors in the stations as well as in the external loading and unloading conveyors. Verticals of this type have been built using sliding-chain conveyors in the station fingers and live-roll or chain conveyors in the external horizontal conveyors.

Unistrand Tray Conveyors

Suspended car verticals are also available using a single continuous strand of chain. The cars are suspended from extended pins on the chain. As the car and load are offset, the car bears against the vertical guides. The friction caused by this offset load is normally reduced by the use of wheels or rollers on the cars.

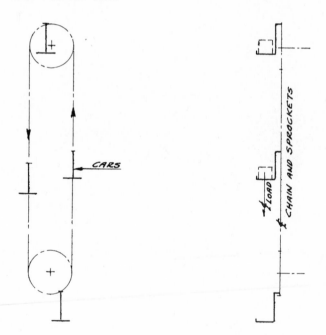

Fig. 11–7. Modified vertical suspended-tray conveyor.

The principle of loading and unloading is similar to that used with the double chain-type vertical previously described, i.e., cars and stations are "finger" construction. Generally, loads are light in weight, and this type of vertical is often used to handle correspondence in trays or containers. One form of this type of conveyor is illustrated in Fig. 11–7.

Opposed-shelf Conveyors

Still another form of vertical conveyor is the opposed-shelf conveyor. The arrangement of such conveyors is shown in Fig. 11–8. As indicated, a conveyor may consist of two or three identical double-strand chain conveyor units. Across each pair of chains are mounted cross members or shelves. The shelves on the opposing elements are kept in alignment by having a common drive medium connecting the two (or three) drive shafts at the top of the conveyor.

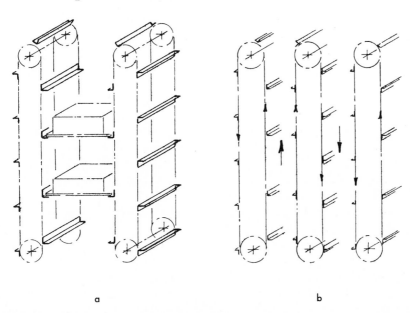

a   b

Fig. 11–8. Opposed-shelf vertical conveyor. (a) Up, down, or reverse service. (b) Simultaneous up and down service.

The load being handled must have a rigid bottom, permitting it to be supported by the two comparatively narrow shelf members at the sides. Such items as tote boxes, pans, trays, shipping crates, pallets, etc., can be conveyed by the opposed-shelf conveyor.

LOADING AND UNLOADING

At the bottom of an up service conveyor, the loading station may consist of a roller or wheel gravity conveyor or any form of power conveyor. The loading conveyor must be narrow enough to enter the vertical path and clear between the edges of the opposed moving shelves.

The load enters the vertical path after one pair of opposing shelves has cleared the loading conveyor and before the next pair of shelves reach the loading conveyor level. The next pair of shelves then lifts the load off the loading conveyor.

At the upper or discharge level, the load must be removed before the shelves open and separate as they turn around their respective sprockets. Several types of unloading devices can be used. One unit consists of a powered conveyor that is hinged at one end, with the free end made to reciprocate up and down. When at the lower level, the hinged conveyor starts to rise at the same speed at which a pair of shelves are moving. It follows the pair of shelves up for a sufficient distance to permit an auxiliary cam arm to push the load off the shelves onto the unloading conveyor. When the load has cleared the vertical path, the hinged unloading conveyor again lowers to the next pair of shelves, ready to receive the subsequent rising load.

A second form of unloading device consists of a rotating and articulated pad or platform that enters the vertical path of the conveyor below the load to be removed. Its upward travel speed is greater than the speed of the moving shelves, and it therefore lifts the load off the opposed shelves. The pad then continues its upward motion and at the same time moves in an arc out of the vertical path of travel. The final travel of the pad or platform is then in a downward arc, depositing the load on conveyor fingers to complete the unloading operation. The pad continues its travel until it again enters the vertical below the next rising load. One complete cycle is made for each pair of opposed shelves.

On the down service conveyors the same loading and unloading devices described above are used. In this case, however, the units are reversed, and the unloading units described above become loading devices. The discharge is accomplished by reversing the direction of travel on the gravity or power conveyors (the loading devices for the up service conveyors).

When heavy loads such as shipping crates or cartons, pallet loads, etc., are handled, the shelves are usually constructed with narrow rollers or wheels to support the loads on their edges. These anti-friction shelves permit loading and unloading units to readily push the heavy loads off or onto the shelves.

If the opposed-shelf conveyor can be stopped during the loading and/or the unloading operations, simple hydraulic or pneumatic pushers can be used to push the load onto or off the shelves. The loading station of an up service conveyor and the unloading station of a down service conveyor can be conventional gravity or power conveyors as previously described. They can, of course, also be operated with the hydraulic or pneumatic pushers. If the pushers are used, the upper and lower stations should be spaced some multiple of shelf spacing. Thus, the loading and unloading operations can be performed simultaneously, and the time of stopping is reduced to a minimum.

As shown in Fig. 11–8, simultaneous up and down service can be obtained on the same machine by using the three-unit conveyor design. The two-conveyor design can, of course, be used for up, down, or reversing service.

Arm Conveyors

The arm conveyor is another form of vertical conveyor. It can be equipped with various types of cars or arms to elevate or lower a variety of items. Some of the more common designs of cars are shown in Fig. 11–9.

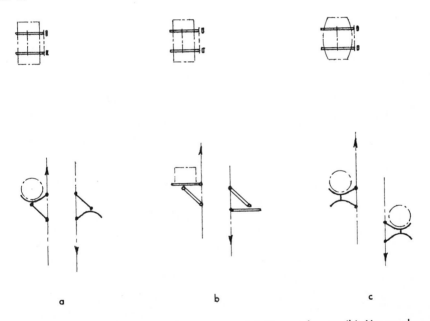

a   b   c

Fig. 11–9. Arm-type vertical conveyor. (a) Up or down. (b) Up or down. (c) Up and down.

Two or more arms are usually provided to support the load. Cross rods or shafts are provided at the articulated joints. Those at the chains extend through and replace the normal chain pins, or they extend through attachments on the chains. When the shafts replace the chain pins, the chain must be of the roller type. The chain then operates in vertical guides, and the chain rollers are subjected to the reactions from the offset load. If the shafts extend through attachments on the chains, the shafts can mount rollers or wheels that operate in guides and so support the offset load. In this latter design the chains are the propelling mediums only, and detachable or pintle chain may be used.

Loading and unloading stations for these conveyors engage the outer edges or rims of the load, but in other respects they are similar in action to the stations described for the opposed-shelf conveyor.

The arm conveyor, when handling round loads, is frequently installed at an angle, and the round load remains on the car as it turns over the upper sprockets. The load then delivers to skids that permit it to roll clear of the now descending arms or cars.

Special-purpose Conveyors

The recent development of a special conveyor is worthy of mention. There are many pieces of equipment described in this book that are priority items with a few manufacturers. The author has not attempted to call attention to every item known to be patented, as such detailed information would be soon obsolete or certainly incomplete. However,

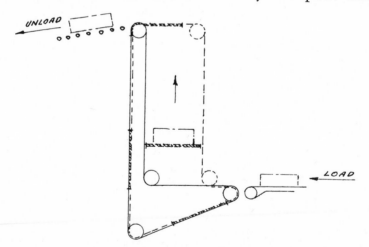

Fig. 11–10. Special-purpose vertical conveyors.

in writing of this new development, it seems advisable to call the reader's attention to the matter of patents because this new design is presently made by only one or two concerns.

The conveyor employs two pairs of chains, operating in some cases over sprockets mounted on common shafts. The unit is illustrated in Fig. 11–10.

The conveying cars or pads consist of a series of closely spaced members that are connected into a unit by two strands of chains or other flexible members. Auxiliary sprockets or wheels guide the pads around the turns. The leading end of the pad is attached to one pair of conveying chains, while the rear end is attached to the other pair of chains.

As loads enter the conveyor, a simple gate or escapement assures that a load will enter only when the leading edge of the pad arrives in a position to receive it. The moving pad automatically pulls the load into the conveyor. The pairs of conveying chains then travel vertically in two separate paths, causing the pad and its load to rise horizontally.

At the upper level, when the leading end of the pad starts to turn the corner and start in a downward direction, the load is automatically delivered to a discharge conveyor or slide.

Reasonably high capacities of about ten loads per minute are possible, and auxiliary loading and unloading stations are not required.

Safety

To assure complete and safe protection to personnel, all vertical conveyors should be automatically loaded and unloaded. The "combing" action of moving cars through stations is particularly hazardous. When a vertical conveyor must be manually loaded or unloaded, the conveyor should be stopped during these operations. A door or gate at the opening to the vertical should be closed before the conveyor can again be started.

Other Vertical Conveyors

There are many other forms of vertical conveyors. The "squeeze" belt, "drag" belt, and belt conveyors with magnets to hold ferrous items are all covered in Chapter 6. Most other types of vertical or steeply inclined conveyors are primarily used for handling bulk material and therefore are not included in this book. Modified forms of vertical traveling buckets mounted on chains or on belting have been employed for handling small unit loads. Also, modified "skip hoists" have been used to raise and lower unit loads such as pallets, tote pans, four-wheel trucks, etc.

12

Pneumatic Conveyors

Pneumatic conveyors are commonly used to convey bulk materials. Such conveyors usually consist of a pipeline into which the dry, pulverized material is introduced mechanically. The material is propelled through the pipeline by compressed air or is moved by suction created by applying a partial vacuum at the discharge end of the line. Various types of collectors or separators are provided to separate the material from the conveying airstream.

Pneumatic conveyors must be considered and evaluated along with belt conveyors, bucket lifts, screw conveyors, etc., when making an analysis of a material-handling problem. The pneumatic conveyor is often used when unit loads are to be handled. Many paper items (single sheets, multiple sheets, correspondence files, rolled or folded blueprints, etc.), as well as other unit loads such as small tools, bottles, and other containers of solids or liquids, can all be successfully conveyed in pressure- or vacuum-actuated air tubes.

Air, either under pressure or vacuum, is also employed to aid gravity, manual, or mechanical handling of unit loads. The gravity type of air-activated conveyor is used extensively in handling bulk material but has also been used for unit loads of comparatively light weight per unit of conveying surface. In handling bulk material, air is introduced into the mass of material for varying distances above the bottom of the conveyor, bin, hopper, ship, car, or truck. The cohesion between the particles in the mass is broken, and the angle of repose is greatly reduced, permitting the material to flow on very shallow grades. When a unit load is to be moved, the cushion of air under the load lifts it free of friction with the graded surface of the conveying medium and permits it to move by the force of gravity. When the unit load is heavy or when it is not practical to move the load by gravity, the air cushion permits the load to be moved manually with very little effort.

Large pieces of fragile material are moved on air conveyors; an example is the handling of sheets of finely finished material that would be marred if conveyed on conventional mechanical conveyors. Another example of handling unit loads on a cushion of air is in moving heavy pallet loads, where an effort of only 4# to 5# is required for each 1,000# of weight.

Air is used to aid mechanical handling of unit loads. The common suction or vacuum cup principle is applied to devices that raise and transport unit loads. One design employs a vacuum head attached to a hoist, crane, lift truck, etc. The head contains a chamber wherein a vacuum is maintained by a centrifugal blower. The face of the chamber is perforated and is usually covered with a porous or open-cell plastic material. This distributes the vacuum evenly over a comparatively large surface. When this head is lowered to a unit load, the suction permits the load to be raised and then conveyed horizontally on equipment similar to conventional cranes.

A group of cartons or similar unit loads may be handled by the vacuum head. It is frequently used in the design of automatic pallet loaders and unloaders. More detail on this device is given in Chapter 13.

It is possible to use a belt conveyor if the belting is made of porous material. The belting then rides across a long vacuum chamber. The loads are held against the belting by atmospheric pressure.

As will be recognized, all air conveyors require special treatment because the design must be adapted to the material or product being handled. This type of conveying is relatively new, and no standardized engineering data are available. Here again, as mentioned in an earlier chapter, it is advisable to use the experience and design data of manufacturers that have built air-operated units.

Carriers

The pneumatic conveyor, using a pipeline to convey unit loads, is an old and proven device. This chapter therefore deals primarily with details of application and design of the conveyor.

In most cases the unit load is enclosed in a carrier for transmission through the pipeline or tube. The standard pipe or line is made of thin-wall steel or aluminum tubing. Installations made in the early years of this century frequently used brass tubing but brass is rarely used today.

Items to be conveyed are sometimes of uniform size and are able to withstand the turbulence in the airstream as well as the impact against the wall as the tube bends or turns. When all of these conditions are favorable, it is possible to convey these items without the need of inserting them into carriers for transmission.

The tubing usually can be obtained with the inside dimension held to a close tolerance so that a maximum size carrier can be used, compatible

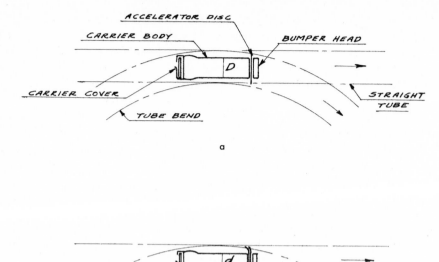

Fig. 12–1. Carriers for pneumatic conveyors. (a) Typical carrier in tubing held to close I.D. tolerance. (b) Typical carrier in tubing having nominal I.D. dimension.

with the clearance needed in negotiating the turns or bends. When the inside dimension of the tubing varies, it is necessary to use a somewhat smaller carrier to accommodate the least dimension of the tube. Figure 12–1 illustrates carriers in the tubes.

In general, a carrier consists of the body, the bumper, the cover or closure, and the accelerator disc(s). Other than the difference in body size, the noticeable characteristic is in the construction of the accelerator disc. In Fig. 12–1(a), the accelerator disc is made of a thin flexible material that fits snugly to the inside of the tubing. In Fig. 12–1(b), the accelerator usually consists of two pieces of material, each having several "slits" extending from the outer edge to the body of the carrier. The slits in the two discs are lapped to avoid air leakage. The outer edges of the discs constantly bend in transit, to conform to the variations in the inside dimensions of the tube. The distance from the tubing wall to the carrier is greater than in the design in Fig. 12–1(a), to permit the flexibility required.

The standard size tubes having constant inside dimensions, with the approximate inside dimensions of carriers, are shown in Table 12–1. The clear inside dimension shown is for a standard message carrier. This dimension will vary with the different lengths of carriers and also with the special-purpose carriers where the body of the carrier requires special construction or is made of other than standard plastic or thin-wall metal.

As will be recognized from Fig. 12–1, especially long carriers may necessitate reducing the size of the body to permit clearance in the tube bends.

Table 12–1. Standard carriers for pneumatic conveyors.

Size of Tube – Inches	Inside Dimension of Carrier – Inches
1-1/2" round	15/16"
2-1/4" round	1-3/8"
3" round	2"
4" round	2-3/4"
6" round	4-1/2"
4" × 7" oval	2-1/2" × 5-9/16"
4" × 12" rectangular*	2-9/16" × 10-7/16"
5" × 13" rectangular*	3" × 11"

*Normally for utility purposes – seldom used for messages.

Carriers used to convey messages vary in length from 4″ to about 14″ in the various size systems. The messages may be single or multiple sheets of paper, usually rolled for insertion in round carriers or folded for the oval carriers. Complete correspondence files can be conveyed in rectangular carriers. The body material in most message carriers is a clear plastic. Other materials—fibre, rubber, leather, and in some cases aluminum—are available as standard in some sizes.

Carriers for special purposes are made from various materials. Examples are: 42″-long aluminum body for rolls of blueprints, tracings, or similar loads, usually in the 4″ round size; aluminum body for groups of punch cards; leather body for bottles or other containers of solids or liquids; leather and/or rubber body for utility use in most sizes; steel body for test pieces in metal-pouring operations; plastic body with special inserts, to convey X-ray film; etc.

Utility of Pneumatic Systems

It is commonly considered that the pneumatic tube using carriers is primarily for commercial and institutional operations. However, it cannot be stressed too strongly that this type of conveyor plays an important part in the handling of material in industrial operations.

The need to keep paperwork flowing evenly, thus keeping pace with production operations, is vital in any industrial plant. Messengers, of necessity, must schedule their "pick-ups" and "drops." When the messenger does arrive, he drops bundles of orders or instructions. The result is a peak load and a period of waiting for the next delivery. In many plants, this inefficient handling of paperwork is noticeable in the shipping department. It is not unusual to have the shipping department cluttered with material ready to be loaded, but the necessary papers and instructions have not arrived. When they do come, at the end of the normal day, the shipping department must work overtime to clear the area for the next day's production. Also, a scheduled truck, train, or plane may be missed because the needed papers did not arrive in time.

The pneumatic tube permits an even flow of paper; the order or other instructions can be dispatched to the shipping or any department as soon as it has been typed or completed. It need not wait until a sufficient group of papers has accumulated to warrant handling by a messenger. One installation in a plant well over a million square feet in size handles almost all its communications by pneumatic tube. It is estimated that tangible savings alone will amortize the investment.

Another example of increased efficiency is in a very small operation where truckers, delivering shipments, had to walk to the cashier's desk to have their invoices paid or approved. A small tube installation eliminated the need for this traffic through the office area.

In addition to handling of papers, there is often a need for replacement or changing of small tools in some operations. A tube system connecting the tool crib with the machine area eliminates the need for the machine operator to walk to the crib.

In a pouring mill a test piece sample is poured from the ladle, and the piece is then dispatched to the laboratory for analysis and report before the entire heat is poured.

The average speed of travel of the carrier in a pneumatic tube is 25 to 35 feet per second. In a multifloor building in which the areas to be served are located on different floors, the difference in time between pneumatic tube and messenger service is more notable.

In many operations, when material-handling equipment is being considered, the pneumatic tube conveyor is an important link in perfecting overall efficiency.

Power Plants

Centrifugal exhausters and blowers are normally employed to create the power to convey the carriers in the line. As the carrier loading is low per square inch of tubing area, the power plant is not required to develop high vacuums or pressures. The range of standard units is from 12 to 24 ounces.

The vacuum-type system is most often used. Figure 12–2 shows a typical arrangement of a simple two-station system. Various types of terminals are available for the stations. Valves keep the air circuit sealed but permit a carrier to be inserted or ejected with only momentary interruption in the flow of other carriers in the line. As illustrated in Fig. 12–2, air enters the system where indicated by the dotted arrow and is exhausted through the centrifugal power plant shown.

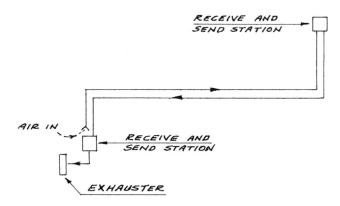

Fig. 12–2. Diagram of pneumatic conveyor.

The size of the power plant depends on many variables, but the following formula will allow the engineer to approximate the vacuum required and the volume of air needed. The friction loss in the conveying line varies with the carrier speed and the number of bends in the line. Tables 12–2, 12–3, and 12–4 are based on a calculated speed of 30 FPS and an average number of bends in the line. The friction loss in the air pipe or the drum at the power plant varies with the air velocity; the values in the tables are based on a velocity of 3,000 FPM. Any 90° elbows in the air pipe should be estimated as equivalent to a length of ten diameters.

$$\text{Total vacuum required, in ounces} = F + f + CR + CH$$

where

$$F = \text{value from Table 12–2}$$
$$f = \text{value from Table 12–3}$$
$$CR = \text{value from Table 12–4}$$
$$CH = \text{value from Table 12–4}$$

The number of carriers likely to be in a line can readily be calculated by assuming even dispatch of X number of carriers per minute or per

Table 12–2. Values of factor F in power calculations for
pneumatic conveyors.

Size of System	Length of Longest Line – Feet	F = Friction Loss – Ounces	Volume – CFM
	Friction Loss F in Conveying Line		
1-1/2" round	300' or less each add. 100'	14 4	35
2-1/4" round	300' or less each add. 100'	11 3	70
3" round	400' or less each add. 100'	9 2	120
4" round	500' or less each add. 100'	9 1-1/2	210
6" round	600' or less each add. 100'	8 1-1/4	450
4" × 7" oval	600' or less each add. 100'	8 1-1/4	400
4" × 12" rectangular	600' or less each add. 100'	6 1	750
5" × 13" rectangular	600' or less each add. 100'	5 1	1100

Table 12–3. Values of factor f in power calculations for
pneumatic conveyors.

Diameter of Pipe or Drum – Inches	f = Friction Loss – Ounces	Diameter of Pipe or Drum – Inches	f = Friction Loss – Ounces
	Friction Loss f in Air Pipe or Drum per 100 Feet		
2"	5.0	12"	0.7
3"	3.4	14"	0.6
4"	2.4	16"	0.5
5"	1.8	20"	0.4
6"	1.4	24"	0.3
7"	1.2	30"	0.2
8"	1.0	36"	0.2
10"	0.8	42"	0.15

Table 12—4. Values of factors CH and CR in power calculations for pneumatic conveyors.

| Size of System | Vacuum Required — in Ounces — To Move a One-Pound* Carrier in Tube Line | |
	Value CH = Vacuum per Carrier, Horizontal Run	Value CR = Vacuum per Carrier, Riser
1-1/2" round	4.00	10.00
2-1/4" round	1.72	4.30
3" round	0.96	2.40
4" round	0.54	1.36
6" round	0.24	0.61
4" × 7" oval	0.28	0.70
4" × 12" rectangular	0.16	0.40
5" × 13" rectangular	0.10	0.26

*Prorate other weights.
  Weight of empty message carrier for approximate purposes:
  1-1/2" – 1/8 lb., 2-1/4" – 1/2 lb., 3" – 1 lb., 4" – 2 lb.
  Approximate the weight of utility carriers or consult manufacturer.

hour. This will determine the number of seconds between dispatches. Assuming a carrier speed of 30 FPS, we can find the estimated feet between carriers. The length of the line is known and the number of carriers likely to be in the line at any time can then be established. The probable spacing will quickly determine if more than one carrier will be in the line and the number likely to be in a riser at a given time.

In a multiple-line system, the vacuum required for the system is based on the requirement for the longest line. If there are only a few long lines and many shorter lines, it may be more economical or practical to use two power plants.

The volume of air required per conveying line is shown in Table 12–2. The total volume required of the power plant is the volume per line multiplied by the number of lines.

Central Desk Systems

The oldest and in many respects the simplest form of pneumatic conveyor system employs a manually operated central station. Figure 12–3 illustrates such a system. As can be seen, complete intercommunication between service points is possible by relaying the carriers at the central station.

All incoming lines from the remote service points discharge their carriers at a central table or slide or onto a power conveyor. Carriers are equipped with identification rings that can be adjusted by the sender to indicate the service point for which the carrier is destined. The central station operator reads the code and dispatches it into the open or intake end of the proper line. In this way any station can send to any other service point as well as to the central station.

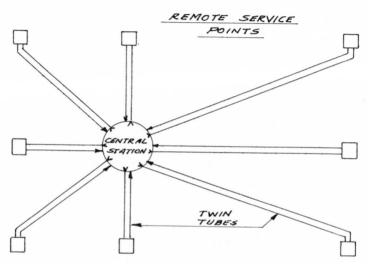

Fig. 12–3. Multiple-line pneumatic conveyor system.

A service station can also be located at the central station, which may be an authorization point or a cashier's station. Usually with this type of operation there is no need for intercommunication between the remote points. Rather, each remote point has business with the central station only. Obviously, with the arrangement shown in Fig. 12–3, it is possible to combine intercommunication with the central control station with individual service.

When comparatively few service points are to be connected, the carriers are discharged onto a gravity slide or a table. The central operator picks the carrier off the receiving slide and dispatches it into the proper outgoing inlet. When many lines are involved, the carriers discharge onto a power conveyor which conveys them to a location where all the outgoing tube inlets are grouped. Thus the operator can perform the transfer from a fixed location.

With the arrangement shown in Fig. 12–3, the power plant is usually located at the central station. All air circuits are tapped into an air drum or pipe leading to the exhauster. The length of each air circuit or line is the total distance from the central station to the remote service point and back to the air drum at the central.

Where low or light traffic justifies their use, modified arrangements using tandem and/or combination lines can be used between two service points. Such arrangements permit the use of one air circuit to serve two remote points. The economies of such modifications can readily be furnished by the manufacturer.

In some operations the flow of traffic does not require the full-time services of the central station operator. In other cases the pneumatic conveyor system is in continuous operation (24 hours a day, 7 days per week). Such an installation would require the services of four central station operators. When an attendant is not required full-time, or when the continuous operation makes manual attention at the central economically unsound, automatic systems should be considered.

Automatic Systems

There are two basic types of automatic pneumatic conveyor designs; one uses a coded carrier, and the other employs an electronic memory device for carrier control.

A typical layout of an automatic system is shown in Fig. 12–4. Thirteen stations are shown on three loops of twin tubes. The number of loops is flexible, and the number of stations on a loop depends on the physical location of the points to be served. Generally it is best to limit the number of stations to about ten per loop.

When coded carriers are used, the desired destination is registered on the carrier before it is dispatched. The carrier travels to the controller where the code is automatically "read" and then diverted into the proper outgoing loop. When the carrier arrives near the destination, its code is again read and a deflector diverts the carrier into the station. If, for example, a carrier for station A4 is dispatched from station C11, it travels to the controller where it is automatically deflected to the A loop; as it reaches station A4 it is ejected from the conveying tube into the station receiver.

When conventional carriers are used, a memory device is located near the controller to govern the flow of the carriers. When a carrier is to be dispatched, it is placed in a dispatch inlet. The desired destination is then indicated by push-button or by a rotary selector (telephone-type dial).

The memory bank "registers" the carrier, and the dispatch inlet is caused to open and admit the carrier into the conveying tube. The arrival of the carrier at the controller is recorded in the memory, and the controller is instructed to direct the carrier to the proper loop. The memory

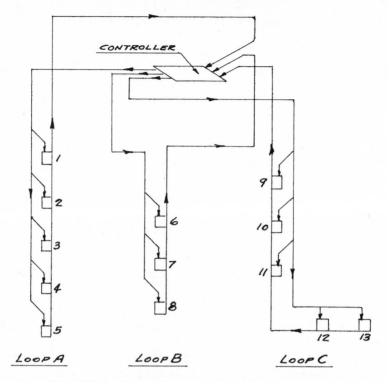

Fig. 12–4. Automatic pneumatic conveyor system.

controls the dispatch of the carrier from the controller and directs the proper deflector to eject the carrier into the station receiver.

SELECTING THE SYSTEM

The selection of the type of automatic pneumatic conveyor—coded carrier or memory control—depends on many factors, and it is advisable to consult the builders of the equipment and benefit by their experience. Some major differences in the two systems can be shown here, to assist in making an analysis. The coded carrier system does not require electrical control wiring between stations. All wiring is confined to local areas at the receiving–dispatch stations and at the controller. The carriers, however, are costlier than conventional carriers. The memory bank system permits the use of economical conventional carriers but requires control wiring between the stations, the memory bank, and the controller. The frequency of service, the number of carriers required to operate the system efficiently, and the distance between service points become economic factors that must be considered in deciding which type of system should be used.

CODING THE CARRIERS

Various methods have been used to carry a code on the carrier. In this author's opinion the most reliable arrangement is to equip round carriers with metallic rings and the oval or rectangular carriers with metallic strips. These rings or strips are electrically connected to indicating rings or dials at one end of the carrier. The indicators are set to designate the receiving station, and this setting makes a partial electric circuit with two of the rings or strips. Brush selectors are located in the receiving tubes of

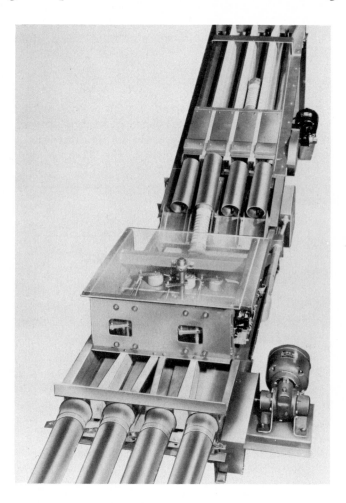

Fig. 12–5. Controller for automatically distributing coded carriers to proper loop containing designated station. (Courtesy Lamson Corporation.)

the controller and in the conveying tubes ahead of each station. The carrier, as it passes through the tube, contacts the brush selectors. When the selector corresponds with the two connected rings or strips, an electrical circuit is completed, and the station deflector is activated to divert the carrier from the line. At the controller, a series of brush selectors "reads" the loop designated and a deflector in the controller diverts the carrier into that loop.

As mentioned above, conventional carriers are used in the memory bank system. The memory bank releases a carrier from the loading inlet at a time when the conveying line is free to receive it. The memory also releases carriers from the controller at timed intervals to assure that the correct carrier will be diverted without interference with other carriers being handled.

SEMIAUTOMATIC SYSTEMS

Modified automatic systems are available for service with a central control or authorizing station. Instead of using a series of twin tubes as illustrated in Fig. 12–3, the same service can be obtained with one set of tubes, as shown in the typical arrangement in Fig. 12–6. In this system a

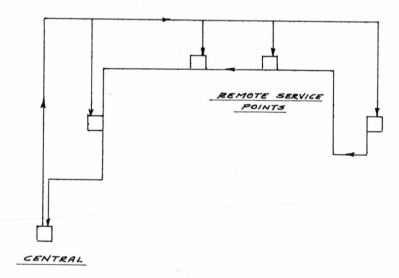

Fig. 12–6. Semiautomatic pneumatic conveyor system.

push-button station is located at the central station. When a carrier is to be sent to one of the remote service points, the operator pushes the button for the station desired. A deflector is actuated at the station, and the carrier is diverted from the line. A signal light at the central station remains on until the carrier arrives at the desired station. After the light goes off, another carrier may be dispatched. Carriers from the remote service points to the central station usually can be dispatched at any time and controlled dispatch inlets are then not required.

This same type of semiautomatic operation can be obtained using coded carriers. In this design, the frequency of dispatch from the central station can be once every five to ten seconds. Carriers from the remote points to the central station may be dispatched at will. This system uses the same brush selectors in the conveying line, and the carrier is automatically diverted from the line as described above for fully automatic operation.

The major advantage of these semiautomatic systems over the conventional central station system shown in Fig. 12–3 is in the reduction of the amount of tubing used. Material and installation costs are less. Also, a marked saving is made in the space required to install the tubes.

13

Pallet Loaders and Unloaders

Automatic pallet loaders and unloaders play an important part in the automated production line. An item may be produced, packed, palletized, and the complete pallet load delivered to the shipping platform by automatic equipment. Likewise, pallet loads may be received at the dock, then delivered to an unloader, and the individual items sent to production or storage by automatic equipment.

Automatic Loaders

The automatic loaders and pallet-loading aids will be discussed first. There are two basic designs of universal automatic loaders. In the one design the individual items are assembled to form a complete layer or tier. The bed on which the layer is formed opens or slides from under the layer, allowing the group of items to drop vertically (in most instances about one inch) onto the pallet or a previously laid layer. In the other basic design the layer is again formed, but the entire layer is picked up by a vacuum head and transported to a position over a waiting pallet. The layer is then lowered and the vacuum released, depositing the layer onto the pallet or a previously laid layer.

Both of these automatic loaders are designed to handle a variety of items: boxes, bundles, cans, cartons, crates, drums, barrels, sacked material, etc. Obviously the nature of some items may dictate which basic design of loader must be used. Some loads may not withstand the action of the layer-forming bed being pulled from under the layer. Other loads are not adaptable to the vacuum head design because the nature of the item will not tolerate the suction, or a vacuum cannot be created.

There are also many special-purpose loaders designed for a specific product. Some of these units follow one of the basic designs of the universal loader. Other specialized loaders use mechanisms that are only suitable for the particular product. This chapter will be confined to a detailed discussion of the universal loaders. If the product cannot be handled by one of the universal units, the engineer may modify a standard unit or design a mechanism that will satisfy the requirements.

LOAD PATTERNS

The pallet load may be formed of columns of items, or it may be desired to form the items into different patterns on alternate or a few layers, to interlock them. Most pallet loads use the interlocked patterns as insurance against disturbing the load while it (the pallet load) is being handled and/or transported.

Fig. 13–1. Automatic pallet loader forming layers on a retracting bed for deposit onto pallet. (Courtesy Lamson Corporation.)

The function of the automatic loader is to receive the items from one or several production lines and form them into complete pallet loads. The individual items are accumulated on conveyors until a sufficient number have collected to complete a pallet load. When a full pallet load has been assembled, a signal is sent to the loader and, if it is free to receive it, the accumulating conveyor begins to discharge the items. A counting device arranges to release only the number of items needed to complete the pallet load.

As the individual items flow to the loader, a turning device at the loader orients the item so that it will assume its proper position and arrangement in the layer.

When the layer has been completed, it is deposited onto the pallet and the next layer is formed. This second layer may require the items to assume the same position as did the items on the first layer, or an entirely different pattern may be desired. The loader automatically forms the various layers in any predetermined manner. After all layers have been laid, the full pallet load is ejected or moved, and another empty pallet moves into position to receive its items.

Several production lines may discharge into a single loader, and each line can be producing different sized items. The signal given to the loader, when a full pallet load of items has accumulated, energizes controls in the loader that arrange the items in the pattern chosen for the particular product on the line. The number of items in a layer and the number of layers in a full pallet load can vary for each production line.

The time required to form a pallet load depends on the number of items in each layer and the number of layers in the load. The number of items that must be turned to orient them into the proper pattern also affects the time required to form the complete pallet load. Usually the time to eject or move a full pallet and position the next empty pallet is offset fully or to some degree by the time needed to form the first layer of the next pallet load.

SYSTEM DESIGN FACTORS

The production in a given installation is normally all one type of load, i.e., boxes, cartons, crates, etc. If the loader manufacturer is given details of the pallet load to be formed—size of items, number of items per load, number of layers, and orientation of items in the layers—he can supply the rate at which the items can be assembled into the pallet load. The production rate of the manufacturing lines will then determine how many production lines can feed one loader.

Probably the best explanation of the above is to follow through the calculations of a hypothetical installation. Assume there are four lines producing sealed cartons of a food product. Line A produces eight 24"-long cartons per minute; Line B produces ten 18"-long cartons per minute; Line C produces fourteen 18"-long cartons per minute; and Line D produces twelve 20"-long cartons per minute. There will be 30 of the A cartons, 40 of the B cartons, 40 of the C cartons, and 36 of the D cartons per pallet load. The loader will palletize carton A at a rate of 45 per minute and cartons B, C, and D at a rate of 50 per minute. Tabulating this information we have:

Carton	Loader Palletizing Rate/Min.	Production Rate/Min.	Cartons per Pallet Load *	Length of Carton Inches *
A	45	8	30	24
B	50	10	40	18
C	50	14	40	18
D	50	12	36	20
		44 total production rate/min.		

* This information is needed in subsequent calculations.

We are now prepared to calculate the total palletizing capacity of the loader from the following formula:

$$\text{Total palletizing capacity} = \frac{45 \times 8}{44} + \frac{50 \times 10}{44} + \frac{50 \times 14}{44} + \frac{50 \times 12}{44}$$
$$= 8.18 + 11.36 + 15.91 + 13.64$$
$$= 49.09$$

The total palletizing rate is greater than the total production rate, and the loader will therefore accommodate the four production lines. Note that there is ample loader capacity but probably not enough excess to permit connecting another production line, unless its rate is extremely low.

The next calculation that must be made is to determine the minimum length of each accumulating line. In the hypothetical example given above we know the number of cartons in each pallet load and the length of the cartons. The formulas for determining the minimum lengths follow:

$$\text{Line for carton } A = \left[30 + \left(\frac{40}{50} + \frac{40}{50} + \frac{36}{50} \right) 8 \right] 0.083 \times 24 \text{ or } 97.12 \text{ feet}$$

$$\text{Line for carton } B = \left[40 + \left(\frac{30}{45} + \frac{40}{50} + \frac{36}{50} \right) 10 \right] 0.083 \times 18 \text{ or } 92.85 \text{ feet}$$

$$\text{Line for carton } C = \left[40 + \left(\frac{30}{45} + \frac{40}{50} + \frac{36}{50} \right) 14 \right] 0.083 \times 18 \text{ or } 104.49 \text{ feet}$$

$$\text{Line for carton } D = \left[36 + \left(\frac{30}{45} + \frac{40}{50} + \frac{40}{50} \right) 12 \right] 0.083 \times 20 \text{ or } 105.61 \text{ feet}$$

As will be seen, the minimum lengths are based on a factor for a length equivalent to the number of cartons in a pallet load multiplied by the length of the carton in feet. To this factor is added the footage of accumulator required to accommodate the cartons being produced during the time the other three cartons are being palletized.

These formulas for accumulating line lengths make no allowance for time lost during the changeover from one pallet-loading operation in the loader to the next. This lost time varies with the physical relation of the accumulating lines to the loader and with the character of the electronic control used by the manufacturer to start the next line after one has completed sending its cartons to the loader. The accumulating lines should always be located as close to the loader as is practical, and the control should permit an accumulated pallet load to follow a previous load within a matter of seconds. To provide for these unknown losses, it is customary to increase the calculated minimum lengths by about 10 per cent.

UNIVERSAL LOADER OPERATION

The data derived from the above formulas will apply to either universal loader. The end of each accumulating line is equipped with a metering conveyor which acts as a stop for the accumulating line and as a measuring device when the accumulator is discharging to the loader. The metering conveyor usually operates at a faster speed than does the accumulating conveyor. Thus, when discharging, the items that have been touching on the accumulator are spaced by the metering conveyor. A counting device—electric eye, limit switch, etc.—counts each item, and when a full pallet load has discharged, the metering conveyor stops and again acts as a block or stop for the accumulator.

The pallet loader signals the various lines that it is ready to receive a load, and the first accumulator that has collected a full complement of items starts to discharge. In any multiple-line system it is always possible that two or more lines have accumulated a full charge simultaneously. Usually a "hunting" device scans the lines in sequence, and the first line in the sequence is the one that is emptied first. The formulas for determining the minimum line length allow for this need to accumulate more than a pallet load.

As the items enter the loader, a counting device again is employed. This device dictates the treatment each item receives, i.e., whether it is to be rotated to orient it properly or whether it is to enter without turning. Likewise, the loader counting device signals when enough items have entered to complete a layer. A mechanism is then actuated to open or slide the bed from under the layer, or the vacuum head is actuated to pick the completed layer off the bed. Also, when a complete complement of items has entered the loader, the completed pallet is moved, and the next empty pallet moves into loading position.

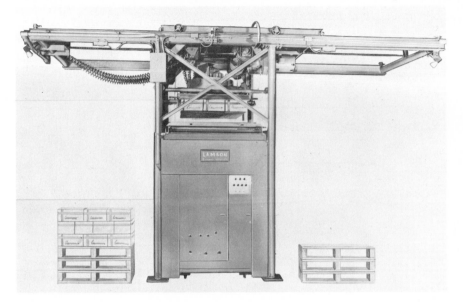

Fig. 13–2. Automatic pallet loader with vacuum head to deposit formed layer onto either of two empty pallet positions. (Courtesy Lamson Corporation.)

The general arrangements of the two types of universal loaders, with their feeding accumulating lines and full pallet discharge, are illustrated in Figs. 13–3 and 13–4. Figure 13–3 shows a loader where the bed opens or slides from under the layer to drop it onto the pallet. In most makes, the orientation of the entrance to the main axis of the loader can be as shown or can be altered to meet requirements. Figure 13–4 shows two possible arrangements. The unit showing two empty pallet positions is used when the full pallet is removed by lift-truck operation. In this case the loader will first fill the pallet on one side and then proceed to fill the other pallet on the opposite side. This allows time for a lift truck to remove the full pallet and replenish the supply of empty pallets.

The other unit in Fig. 13–4 indicates a powered conveyor to automatically move a full pallet out of position and replace it with an empty pallet. With this arrangement full pallets may be accumulated, or they may be transported to a remote point for removal by lift trucks.

In both figures an empty pallet dispenser is shown. Such units are normally automatically operated, and the dispensing action is triggered by the main control in the loader.

Many loaders employ electric motors to operate the various mechanisms. Others use hydraulic and/or air-operated mechanisms. There are many variations in detailed operation of the different makes of loaders,

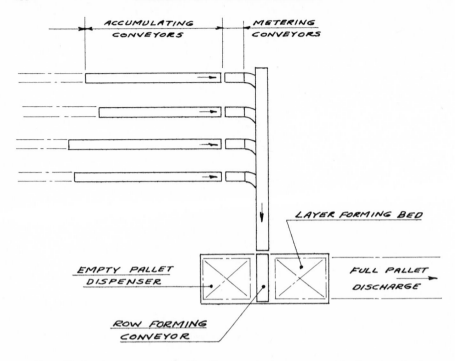

Fig. 13–3. Automatic pallet loader employing retractable forming bed.

but the illustrations show the basic principles of the two most common types.

In either design, the items after leaving the metering conveyors at the accumulators enter the row-forming conveyor, spaced to permit a turning device to rotate those items that must be turned to form the pattern required. Figure 13–5 shows one pattern and illustrates how rows and layers are formed. The completed layers are shown to illustrate a possible arrangement of forming an interlocked load. Also shown are the individual rows of the bottom layer before they transfer from the row-forming conveyor to the layer-forming bed.

The first row consists of three items with the first item rotated. The second row consists of two items. The third row consists of three items with the last rotated. The fourth row consists of two items.

As each row is completed, it is transferred to the layer bed. Note that in the first and third rows the rotated item is spaced from the other items in the row. This space allows clearance when the following rows are transferred, to be certain that the item passing the one rotated, already on the bed, does not touch and dislodge it. After all items for the layer have been transferred to the bed, a compacting device closes all clearance spaces. The layer is now ready for transfer to the pallet, by lowering it when the bed either opens or slides from under it, or is ready for transfer by a vacuum head.

All motions are automatic from the time the items enter the accumulating conveyors until the completed pallet load has been formed and in some cases has been transferred to a convenient point for handling by lift trucks. In most designs the various motions are performed sequentially by the operation of stepping switches. The impulses to these switches are given when items pass the counting device as they enter the loader.

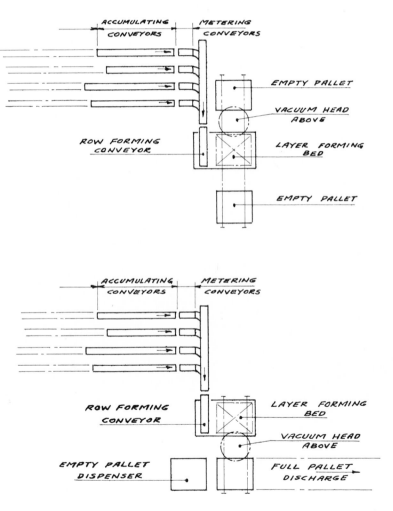

Fig. 13–4. Automatic pallet loader employing vacuum head.

In the pattern shown in Fig. 13–5, the first item entering is caused to rotate and a stop in the row-forming conveyor is actuated to keep the following two items spaced from the one rotated. After the third item has entered, the transfer mechanism is actuated. When the row-forming conveyor is clear, the next two items enter and rest at the stop position; this

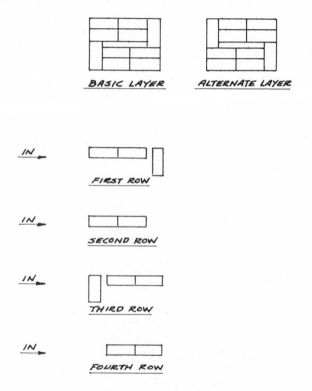

Fig. 13–5. Typical layer arrangement for pallet loader.

second row is then transferred to the layer-forming bed. In many designs the rows being transferred push items previously transferred ahead on the bed. After all rows in a layer have been transferred and compacted, the layer is transferred to the pallet.

During the transfer from the layer-forming bed to the pallet, the first row of the following layer may be formed on the row-forming conveyor. Many operations in the loader can be similarly performed in concert and the capacity of the loader is thereby increased.

A control box, containing the devices that dictate the various motions, is supplied for each pallet load to be assembled by the loader. The proper control box is automatically entered in the circuit when an accumulating line is triggered to discharge its complement of items.

In the loader illustrated in Fig. 13–3, the empty pallet is elevated to a position just below the layer-forming bed. This bed is usually a metal plate that may be constructed in two pieces. When the layer is ready to be lowered to the pallet, the two halves open and the layer drops to the pallet. In other designs the bed is a single plate or may be constructed of closely spaced rollers. The roller bed can be used only when the items being handled can tolerate the additional drop that the thicker roller bed requires.

After each layer is deposited, the pallet is lowered until the bed can be closed to receive the next layer. When the last layer has been deposited, the pallet is lowered fully and deposited onto a conveyor for movement out of the loader. Any type of pallet may be used, including those made of a sheet of paper or other thin material.

A complete load may be assembled without the use of a pallet. When this is desired, the elevating and lowering mechanism is usually constructed with a power conveyor bed (belt, slat, or drag-chain type). The bottom layer is deposited on this immobile conveyor. When the pallet load is completed, the conveyor is lowered until it is in line with the discharge system. The conveyor is then activated and the pallet load is transferred to the system which removes it from the loader.

The loader may be equipped with a variety of accessories, such as gluing units which automatically apply glue to the individual items (usually cartons) to form a cohesive load; marking devices to code the load; banding units that completely tie the top layer (usually) into a solid mass; devices to insert sheets of paper or similar thin material between layers.

In the design of the loader shown in Fig. 13–4, the layer-forming bed can be a metal plate or a bed of rollers, either idle or driven. In this design the thickness or depth of the layer-forming bed is immaterial. When the layer is completed and compacted, if needed, the vacuum head lifts it off the bed and transfers it to a pallet. The vacuum head is constructed of a plenum with a perforated face that is usually covered with a porous material. Some designs use a low-vacuum high-volume exhauster. The outer perimeter of the head is equipped with a flexible skirt that effectively surrounds the layer to seal off voids and prevent excessive loss of suction. With a high-vacuum low-volume type of exhauster, the head face has strips of non-porous material arranged to seal off the spaces between the individual items in the layer.

With either type exhauster, the vacuum is created when the head lowers to the layer of items. The head is then raised and moved until it registers over the waiting pallet. The head is lowered until the layer contacts the empty pallet or a previously laid layer. The vacuum is then released and the layer remains on the pallet while the head returns to a position over the layer-forming bed to await the completion of the next layer.

The loader shown in Fig. 13–4 may also be equipped with accessories for gluing, coding, etc., as described for the other universal loader; however, some accessories are not as readily applied.

SPECIAL LOADERS

In addition to the universal loaders there are special-purpose units designed for a specific kind of item or unit load. Many of these special-purpose units have been installed in sufficient numbers to become standards in their field. These units are made by several manufacturers. Some special-purpose units are: a loader that stacks soft-drink flats or similar items—usually in column form, not in interlocked patterns; loaders for palletizing oil drums—normally one layer high; rolled goods such as roofing paper where the rolls are assembled on end on the pallet—normally one layer high; loaders for nail kegs and boxes or any other items that are too heavy to be handled easily by the universal loaders.

Many pallet-loading aids are designed to reduce to a minimum the effort needed to form a pallet load manually. One such unit consists of a turntable with a top large enough to accommodate two pallets and with high guards or guides fixed to the table. One pallet is loaded by an operator removing items from a conveyor and placing them onto the pallet, using the guards as a gauge to assure alignment of the items with two sides of the pallet. When one load has been formed, the turntable is rotated, and an empty pallet is again presented to the loading operator. The completed pallet load is now in a position where it can be removed readily by a lift-truck operator and an empty pallet is put into position on the table, without interfering with the operator placing items on a pallet.

Another aid consists of an elevating mechanism with or without a turntable top. A pallet can then be presented to an operator stationed on a raised platform, so that as he places a layer on the pallet, it is lowered one layer height until the full complement of layers has been placed. In this way the loading operator does not have to "stoop" or "lift" as would be the case if the pallet were placed on or near the floor level. If the device is equipped with a turntable top, the pallet can be rotated so that the operator does not have to "reach" to place the items. This latter aid has been used to assist in manually unloading or removing items from a pallet by reversing the operation described above.

Another aid which should probably be classed as a semiautomatic loader, assumes the general outline of the universal loader illustrated in Fig. 13–3. In this conception, an operator is located at the row-forming conveyor. The operator rotates items as required and, when a row is completed, he transfers it to the layer-forming bed. The operator uses a push-button panel to initiate the operations of sliding the bed from under the layer, controlling the vertical movement of the pallet, etc. This semi-automatic loader is adaptable to low production rates and usually to one or a very few production lines.

Automatic Unloaders

Automatic pallet unloaders take many forms. One unit consists of a conveyor that delivers a full pallet to a station where clamps engage the entire load and lift it off the pallet. The pallet is then removed from under the load. The clamp device then lowers the load to the now immobile bed, disengages, elevates, and reengages all but the bottom layer. The clamp device again raises all the upper layers, and the bed moves the bottom layer from under the load. After the layer is removed, a series of conveyors and other mechanical motions unscrambles the layer so that the items are dispatched in single file on a conveyor system. The operation is repeated until the entire pallet load has been unscrambled.

Another type of unloader employs the vacuum head principle. The head lowers onto the pallet load, engages the top layer, lifts it, and moves it to an unscrambling system. This design is suitable for any items adaptable to handling by vacuum.

Still another type of automatic unloader uses an electromagnetic head in place of the vacuum head. Obviously this unit is adaptable only to items that have ferrous tops or are made of iron or other magnetic metal. The layers should be separated by sheets of insulating material to avoid failures.

14

Storage

The method of operation, combined with economics, usually will dictate the type of storage rack that should be used. Also, an analysis will indicate whether a change in the method of operation should be considered. In a manufacturing plant, where it is necessary to store partially completed components between operations, there are two general classifications of storage principles available—"dead" or "live" storage.

In dead storage the component is moved to an area where shelving or racks are arranged to hold it. If the parts are handled on pallets, lift trucks or stackers can be used to load and unload the racks or shelves. These handling units can be used if the components are bundles of round objects or stacks of sheets or plates. The stackers may be mobile units operating on the floor, or they may be the overhead crane type.

Fully automatic tiering units are frequently employed to handle pallets in aisles between tiers of racks. These stackers and tiering units generally permit operation in aisles too narrow for conventional lift-truck operation. The unit travels the length of the racks, stops at the correct station and elevates to the proper level to place the load into the rack. On the return trip, the unit can remove a load from the rack and deliver it at the end of the aisle. The entire operation is electronically controlled, and the operation of the unit is determined by a dispatcher with a push-button console. The pallets can be conventional type, or they may be plain metal plates or sheets of plywood.

If racks are used, the construction is indicated by the shape of the component. If the bottoms are flat as would be the case if pallets are used, the racks can be simple skeletal structures. If bundles of components are stored, the racks can have horizontal supporting arms with vertical separators, or the supporting arms may be sloped (commonly known as "tree" racks). If bundles are to be stored, they can be handled in the rack area with overhead cranes, and lift trucks or stackers may not be necessary.

If live storage is used between operations, a conveyor of the roller, live-roll, or overhead trolley type can be used. With this method the components are not removed from the conveyor and first in–first out operation can be realized. Live storage normally is practical when the quantity of items to be stored is relatively small. The roller conveyor or the live-roll conveyor is usually applied when the distance between operations is short and when it is practical to utilize the floor space that these conveyors use. The overhead trolley conveyor utilizes "air space" by elevating the items, circulating overhead, and then lowering the parts to an unloading point(s). With this latter conveyor any aisles between operations can be kept clear for floor traffic.

Generally in any operation where material is received in large lots, such as pallet loads, and shipped in these same lots, the storage racks take one of two forms. They may be skeletal structural racks or they may be equipped with sections of roller conveyor.

Most large loads such as pallets are handled by lift trucks or by stackers (either floor or overhead crane type). Lift trucks are normally used to handle pallet loads on both the receiving and shipping docks. Therefore,

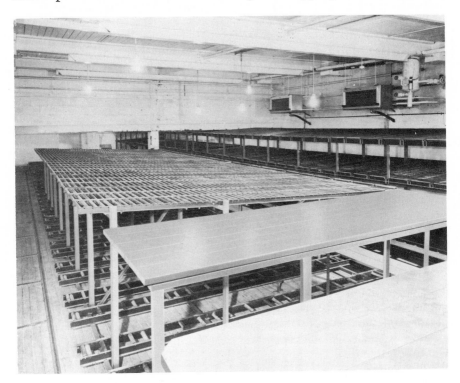

Fig. 14–1. Roller conveyor storage racks. (Courtesy Lamson Corporation.)

it is probably more economical to use the trucks to service the storage area. If aisle space between racks is at a premium, stackers should be considered.

In some operations, especially where perishable items are handled or where it is necessary to ship items on a first in–first out basis, roller conveyor racks are used. The large loads are normally too heavy to handle in gravity-roller racks. The conveyor should therefore be level or, if

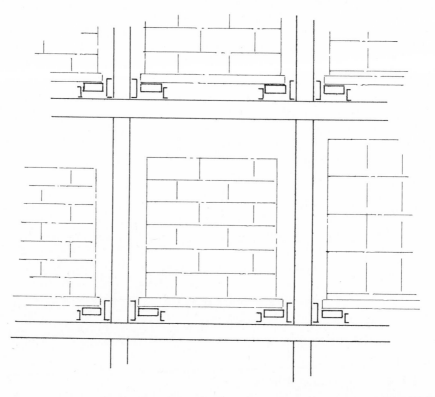

Fig. 14–2. Storage racks for pallet loads.

graded, the drop should not exceed about $\frac{3}{16}''$ per foot or 2″ in ten feet. This recommended grade is for conventional wood pallets; if pallets are equipped with metal runners or the pallets are flat metal plates or sheets of plywood, the grade should be half that used for the conventional pallet.

The grade used should not permit the load to flow by gravity. If the load being handled has any special feature, the optimum grade can be readily established in a test using a section of the roller conveyor that will be used.

The lift-truck operator, when placing a load into the rack, can push previously placed loads ahead to make space for the new load. The conveyor rack should be limited to about 4 to 6 pallet loads in length. Longer racks have been used, but generally auxiliary pushing devices are then used to advance all loads toward the unloading end for ready access to the trucks removing the pallets from storage. In some installations the pallets are advanced manually, but such arrangements require catwalks to permit the operators to move easily from lane to lane in the rack. To allow the operators freedom of movement, this arrangement requires a greater floor area than does the rack equipped with mechanical pushers.

The conveyor used in these racks can be constructed of two narrow lanes, as illustrated in Fig. 14–2. This construction is commonly used when the conveyor is on a single level, laid on or near the floor. An operator can then safely walk between the conveyor lanes and manually advance the load. The effort per 1,000# of load varies from 20# on level lines to as little as 5# on graded lines.

In any operation where items are to be stored for long periods or where items are received in bulk loads and removed from storage in small quantities, conveyorized racks may be indicated. Such requirements are found in all types of warehouse operation. The warehouse may be a part of a manufacturing unit where finished products are stored prior to release on shipping orders. Or the warehouse may be a separate operation, such as in any wholesale merchandising business where manufactured and/or processed items are received in bulk and shipped in broken lots.

This type of warehouse operation, which requires a careful analysis to determine the best method of operation and the best kind of storage rack, will be primarily dealt with in this chapter.

The Decision to Automate

Probably the first step before discussing equipment details is to review some factors that affect overall design planning. Because items are received in large lots such as pallet loads and are shipped in broken lots, the labor cost of picking orders for shipment is greater than the labor cost of putting the items into storage. Picking is, then, the area that receives the most attention when an automatic system is being planned.

In most warehousing operations there are a comparatively few items that represent a high percentage of the tonnage shipped. Frequently, therefore, when automatic picking is being considered, the tendency is to confine the automated system to the fast moving or high-volume items. When the cost of the system is then balanced against tangible savings, it is often found that such tangibles do not warrant the installation. In any manual picking operation, the pickers arriving in a popular item area can pick a high percentage of the pieces on the order with practically no time lost in traveling. Inversely, when picking slow-moving items, they spend much of their time in traveling from rack position to rack position. Therefore, if only the most popular items are planned to be handled by an automatic picking system, the greater part of the labor cost remains, and it is difficult to justify the investment on tangible savings alone.

It does not follow that all items should be included in a plan to automate the picking operation, nor should consideration of such a system be abandoned because to include all or most of the items would apparently make the initial investment too expensive. Many automatic picking systems now in operation are economically sound because intangible benefits justify them. Better control of inventory, faster service in filling orders (some orders can be en route to the customer in an hour), less pilfering, safer handling of fragile items, savings in floor space—these are some of the intangibles that should be evaluated.

Also, the charging or loading of the racks should be analyzed. In spite of the lower labor cost for manual loading, there are also many losses in tangible savings in this area that must be evaluated. Automatic loading systems are available, and this author feels that automation of the loading area, while more difficult to solve satisfactorily, has been neglected by designers.

There are always items that are not adaptable to handling by a conventional, universal automatic system. Such items are usually low-volume pieces that can be handled manually. If some of these items are popular and represent a high volume, it is possible that a special-purpose handling unit can be economically designed.

In the following discussion of the various methods of operation and the different kinds of equipment available, the factors mentioned above should be kept in mind.

Warehouse Layouts

Figure 14–3 shows a typical warehouse layout. In this plan the racks are simple skeletal structures in which filled pallets are placed by lift trucks operating in the service aisles. The pallets are stored on two levels.

Pickers, pulling carts through the picking aisles, remove the desired number of items from the pallets in the lower level. The pallet in the upper tier holds the same item as the pallet immediately below it. When the picker sees that the lower supply pallet is down to a minimum number of pieces, he operates a signal which indicates "empty" in the service aisle.

A lift-truck operator removes the lower, used pallet and replaces it with the full pallet from the tier above. Any few remaining items on the used pallet are placed on top of the items on the filled pallet that he places in the lower tier. The truck operator then removes the empty pallet and

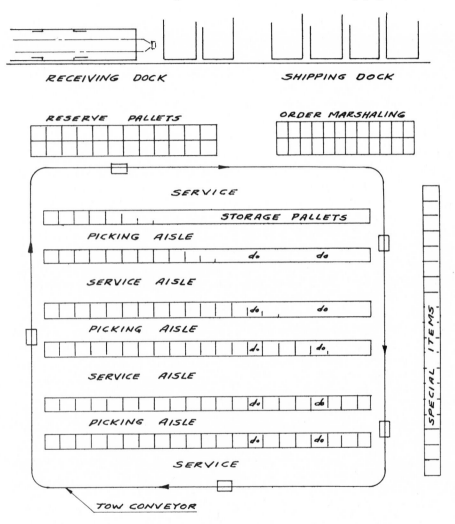

Fig. 14–3. Storage warehouse arrangement with tow conveyor.

brings in a new, filled pallet load of the same item and places it in the upper tier.

If the truck operator cannot lower the reserve pallet in time to accommodate the next pickers, items can be picked from the reserve pallet until the supply has been replenished in the more convenient lower position. Fast moving items may be assigned to two or more rack positions to avoid unnecessary delays.

When a picker has filled his cart or has completed an order, he moves to the nearest aisle exit and connects the cart to the tow conveyor. This conveyor delivers the filled carts to the order-marshaling area at the shipping dock. The tow conveyor continuously conveys empty carts in the circuit, and the picker disengages an empty when he dispatches his filled cart. Truck traffic can cross the path of the tow conveyor between the moving carts.

The tow conveyor can be arranged to discharge the empty carts automatically at points near the ends of the picking aisles. Also, filled carts can be automatically disengaged from the conveyor in the marshaling area. The tow system can be further automated by dispatching carts with orders to selected stations in the marshaling area and so keep shipping orders separated.

The same warehouse layout is possible without the installation of a tow conveyor. If the volume of pieces shipped is low, the pickers may have time to deliver their filled carts to the marshaling area and return to the picking aisles with an empty cart.

Figure 14–4 shows an alternate arrangement in the same warehouse. Here the picking aisles are equipped with stackers on which the picker rides. The stacker straddles a conveyor on the floor. The picker can elevate his platform so that he can readily reach items on pallets in either tier. With this arrangement it is possible to store pallet loads on more than two levels. Attached to the stacker is a conveyor with one end attached to the picker's platform and the other end free to move over the floor conveyor. In this way, as the stacker platform changes elevation, the attached conveyor assumes different angles of decline.

As an item is picked, it is placed on the declined conveyor which in turn delivers it to the floor conveyor. Loads are then conveyed to the order-marshaling area. Non-interference devices are located at the conveyor junctions. Since different orders may be picked simultaneously, the orders must be segregated in the marshaling area.

For a given area, the racks cannot be as long as the racks in the arrangement in Fig. 14–3. The trailing declined conveyor on the stacker requires that more space be available at the right end of the picking aisle to enable the stacker to reach the pallets stored at the extreme right. The decrease in length of racks is offset by the ability to store different items on two or more levels. All of them can be easily reached by the picker. More items can then be stored in a given area in spite of the shorter length of the racks.

An alternate is to have a separate conveyor system from each picking aisle to the marshaling area. This makes the assembly of orders an easier task. Carts are not used and the picker is not required to walk in performing his operations. A greater number of items may be stored in the

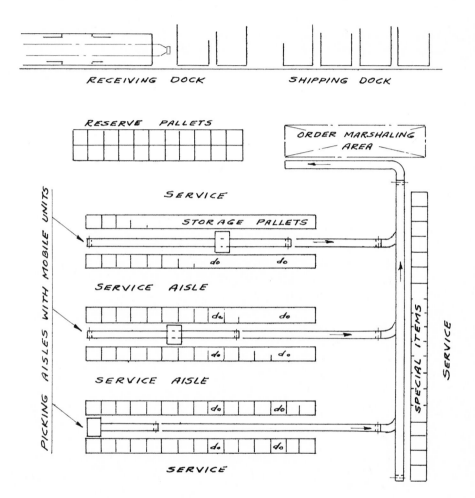

Fig. 14–4. Storage warehouse arrangement with belt conveyors.

aisle. When a picker is assigned to one aisle, he can pick at a faster rate than if he had to remember the location of items in all the aisles.

Lift trucks can only enter from one end of the service lanes because the conveyor system closes off the other ends.

Of the two systems described above, the one shown in Fig. 14–3 is the more popular, probably because it is considered more flexible by many but more likely because it is an older conception.

PICKER EFFICIENCY

Still another method of aiding pickers in performing their work at a greater rate is shown in Fig. 14–5. In this arrangement, the pallet loads are stored on short sections of roller conveyor that have been graded slightly to enable the pallets to be easily pushed or pulled to advance them to the picking aisle. The lift-truck operators keep each lane supplied with filled pallets.

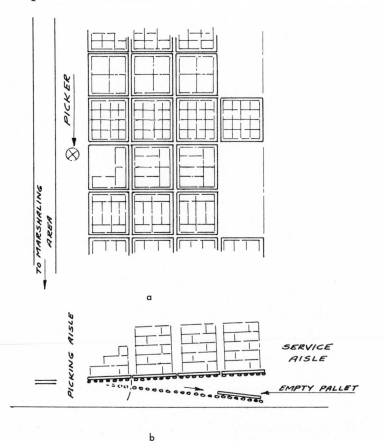

Fig. 14–5. Arrangement of pallet loads for picking operation. (a) Plan. (b) Elevation.

The picker remains in a relatively small area, usually being assigned to pick 4 to 12 items. The number of assigned items depends on the movement or popularity of the items. If all are slow-moving items, he may be assigned to more than 12. If all items are fast-moving, it may be necessary to assign as few as 4. As he removes the required number of pieces from each storage lane, he places them onto the conveyor leading to the order-marshaling area.

When the supply on a pallet has been exhausted, the picker allows the hinged section of conveyor to swing down and the empty pallet is returned to the service aisle for removal by the lift-truck operator. The presence of an empty pallet is an automatic signal to the truck operator to bring in a new pallet load from the bulk reserve area.

When the picker has disposed of the empty pallet, he raises the hinged section of conveyor into position and pulls the next pallet into the picking zone. This arrangement increases the picking rate because the picker spends very little time in performing other duties and is not required to travel through the entire storage area.

In the above examples of manual picking of shipping orders, the arrangement chosen may depend on the method of assigning orders to the pickers. If a picker is given an entire order to pick, an arrangement similar to that shown in Fig. 14–3 would be the most suitable. Whether this arrangement included a tow conveyor would depend on the volume of pieces that have to be picked. If the order is divided into groups of items stored in each picking aisle or area, the arrangements shown in Figs. 14–4 or 14–5 would probably be used. Also, these latter arrangements can be used if orders are combined so that groups of orders calling for the same items are picked simultaneously. In either case, the items must be separated into shipping orders in the marshaling area.

When the volume is large enough, the possibility of using automatic picking should be investigated. There is no degree of volume that can be used as a norm to determine whether automatic picking is indicated. As previously mentioned, there may be intangible considerations that will prevail. There are, however, certain factors that can be used in making an analysis of the warehouse operation.

The picker, removing an item from stock and marking it with a code to designate order and route number, can load a cart or conveyor at a rate of 8 to 14 items per minute. The rate will depend on the number of digits in the code and the size and weight of the piece handled. Pulling a cart, the picker can walk at a rate of 150 to 200 FPM. The time he spends moving from rack position to rack position must be deducted from his available picking time. Also, a fatigue factor must be considered. This factor may be as low as 20 per cent and as high as 35 per cent. Again,

Fig. 14–6. Manual picking operation. When order is complete, the carton or tote is pushed to the belt conveyor for delivery to shipping area. (Courtesy Lamson Corporation.)

the weight of the item plus the convenience of the piece location affect the degree of fatigue.

In any warehouse operation where manual picking is employed, accurate figures for the various factors can be determined and then applied in the analysis.

Storage Racks

The following discussion of storage racks for automatic picking operations covers all types available at the present stage of development. Any type of automatic rack usually operated by gravity and designed for mechanized picking can also be used for manual picking. Items are stored in single file in the different lanes of the rack. As soon as a piece is removed, the entire line of pieces advances so that a piece is always at a convenient place at the front of the rack.

When manual picking is employed, the use of automatic racks presents the pieces to the picker at an easily reached point; he need not reach into the storage area to retrieve a piece. Many more items can be presented to the picker in a given front area of the rack, thereby reducing travel time.

The picking rate is greater with an automatic rack. Also, the rack assures that items will be picked on a first in–first out basis.

In the discussion of automatic racks, various types of mechanical escapements are also covered. It is possible to modify any of these arrangements of racks and escapements into semiautomatic operation. It may be practical and in some cases advisable to use manual control in place of automatic control in some phases of the operation.

Fig. 14–7. Manual order picking from racks to takeaway belt conveyor. (Courtesy Mathews Conveyer Company.)

The majority of automatic racks consist of lanes of gravity conveyors—slides or chutes, wheel or roller conveyors. All items that are stored in the racks have riding surfaces suitable for travel on the conveyors. Cartons, boxes, and other containers make up the bulk of items stored.

LANE WIDTH

Since all items stored in any lane are identical, the accumulation of such loads on the conveyor lane is practical. The width of the lane is such that the pieces are maintained in alignment. It is not necessary to use a different width of lane for every variation of load width. Good operation can be realized by grouping loads so that all those in one group can be accumulated in a lane width suitable for the widest load in the group. The variation in width of loads for any one lane, however, should not be too great. If the narrowest load in a group is 12″ wide while the widest is 20″, there may be difficulty in keeping the narrower loads in alignment; also, considerable storage area is wasted when a wide lane is used to store narrow loads. However if, to reduce waste space, the lane widths are varied too greatly, the cost of the rack may be increased because of the large number of different widths. Also, if lane widths are varied to accommodate each load size exactly, there is no margin available for a change in the package size, which is inevitable.

Assume that we are to store cartons varying from 8″ wide to 24″ wide and the total volume makeup is as follows:

Width (inches)	Per Cent of Volume
8	12
10	10
12	10
14	18
16	13
18	15
20	12
22	6
24	4

If we group the 8″- to 12″-wide loads we have 32 per cent of volume. If those 14″ to 18″ wide are grouped, they represent 46 per cent. The 20″- to 24″-wide loads represent 22 per cent. To allow for future changes in carton widths, the lanes could be designed as follows:

> 25 per cent of lanes for widths to 12″
> 45 per cent of lanes for widths to 18″
> 30 per cent of lanes for widths to 24″

It is always possible to store one of the narrower loads in a wider lane by installing auxiliary guardrails to keep loads properly aligned. A variation in lane widths, somewhat as is given in the above example, is a good compromise to avoid an excessively high-cost rack and to minimize wasted storage space.

SLIDES

If chutes or slides are used in the lanes, the grade or drop will depend on the type of material used in the slide, the construction of the slide, and the type of load, i.e., carton, wood or metal container, etc. The material used in constructing the slide is normally a rust-resistant metal such as galvanized steel or aluminum. Stainless steel is seldom used. The construction most often used is illustrated in Fig. 14–8. As will be seen, with this construction the width variation in loads cannot be too great. The open-center construction is more readily adapted to full and empty lane signal actuators and to escapement mechanisms. The open structure also permits satisfactory operation at grades less than would be required in a solid-bed construction.

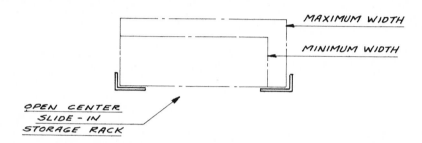

Fig. 14–8. Arrangement of slide-type lane in storage rack.

The grade or angle of decline will vary from 15° to 20° for cartons at normal room temperatures. If frozen foods are stored in the racks and the area is subject to regular defrosting conditions, this construction may prove troublesome. The packages may freeze to the slide when the area is frozen again. In this type of application it is customary to install plastic rods or narrow strips in the slide to keep the packages free of the metal slide. Variation in width of packages that can be handled in the same lane will be more limited. If plastic strips are used, the minimum grades will suffice.

The slide type of rack, because of the rather steep drop required—3″ to 4½″ per foot—can only be used where there is ample elevation. Figure 14–9 shows a possible arrangement of this type of rack. Note that the area under the high end of the rack is utilized for storage of bulk material. The illustration shows one takeaway conveyor for every two levels of storage lanes. The number of these conveyors that will be required depends on the product handled and the service required, as will be shown later.

WHEEL AND ROLLER CONVEYORS

Wheel or roller gravity conveyors can be used in the rack. The drop required for these types of conveyors is about ¾″ to 1″ per foot. In this type of rack the grade required is much greater than would be required for the same conveyors used in conventional conveyor lines. In the latter case, the loads are moving almost constantly; when they are stopped occasionally, it is only for very short periods. When used in storage racks, the loads will be at rest for long periods—as long as 63 hours over a normal weekend, and 87 hours when either Friday or Monday is included in a holiday weekend.

When the loads—especially cartons, which make up the majority of loads stored—remain standing for these long periods, the bottoms of the loads droop over the wheels or rollers and leave small indentations in the bottoms. When it is necessary for the loads to move down the conveyor again, the load must be lifted to permit it to advance. This extra effort

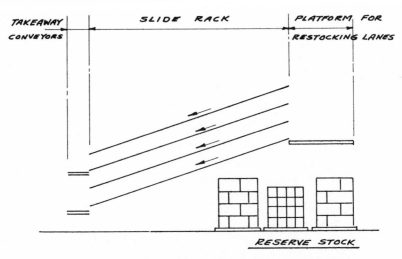

Fig. 14–9. Arrangement of slide-type storage rack.

requires grades at least twice that normally used for the same conveyor handling the same load on a conventional conveyor system. If the storage area is subject to atmospheric changes, the high humidity conditions will cause the carton stock to absorb moisture and the droop will be more pronounced. Roller conveyors present a greater area of load support than do wheel conveyors. Cartons tend to droop less on the rollers. It is for these reasons that the grade required is about the same for wheel or roller conveyor racks. In conventional conveyor systems the grade required for wheel conveyors is considerably less than that required for roller conveyors. (See Chapter 5.)

In any gravity storage lane, it is essential that the drop or degree of decline of the conveyor be enough to assure quick starting of the following loads when the first piece has been removed. The action must be fast

Fig. 14–10. Discharge end of three-level storage rack with escapements and collecting conveyors. Punch cards are used to pick loads automatically from rack. (Courtesy Alvey-Ferguson Company.)

enough to assure that another load will be quickly available for discharge if two or more are to be ejected from the same lane successively. To facilitate this quick movement, the declines should be no less than those described above, unless exhaustive tests made under exact operating conditions have determined a more suitable grade.

LANE LENGTH

Any workable grade will result in pressure being exerted by the line of loads in the storage lane. The magnitude of pressure increases as the number of loads in the lane increases, and the first load must resist the maximal pressure. This first load is also the one that is restrained by the stop or escapement mechanism. The magnitude of the pressure is about 8# for each 100# of total accumulated load. Generally the lanes should not be long—usually not over 30 feet. Lanes 50 feet in length have been used where the load was capable of withstanding the pressure or where extremely light loads were stored. These ideal conditions, however, are seldom encountered.

If a roller conveyor is used in the storage rack, the rollers in the conveyor can be of a light-duty type. In a conventional roller conveyor system the flow may be continuous at about 60 FPM, and usually the handling rate is such that the rollers are turning continuously. Assuming that the rollers are 2″ in diameter, a roller will make 120 revolutions each minute or a total of 57,600 revolutions in 8 hours. These rollers would also be subject to frequent shock loading where packages are deposited at any point in the system. In a storage lane, the rollers are idle the greater part of the day. If we assume 100 withdrawals from the lane in

Fig. 14–11. System of collecting belts delivering loads from rack to truck docks. (Courtesy Alvey-Ferguson Company.)

an 8-hour day and further assume a package length of 24″, the 2″ rollers will make only 400 revolutions in 8 hours. Also, the only shock to the rollers will occur at the loading end of the lane where provisions can readily be made to absorb the impact. The rollers in the conveyor of a storage rack are therefore subjected to less than 1 per cent of the wear they would receive in a conventional conveyor system.

The wheels used in a wheel conveyor are of light construction, and the same units are used in conveyor systems and in storage racks. It is possible that fewer wheels per unit length can be used in the rack conveyor because of the less severe service. However, if cartons or other soft-bottom loads are being stored, the number of wheels under a load should not be decreased to the extent that the cartons will droop badly and excessive grade will be required to start them from rest.

POWERED STORAGE LANES

Power conveyors may be used in the storage lanes when gravity-actuated conveyors are not suitable. A lane may consist of two parallel sections of roller conveyor with a mechanical pusher used to advance the loads to the discharge end of the lane. An example of this construction is shown in Fig. 14–12. The pusher in this case is a belt conveyor installed slightly above the level of the roller conveyors. As long as there is no resistance, the load will be advanced by the frictional contact with the moving belt. As soon as the load is stopped at the escapement or by previously accumulated loads, the belting will slide or slip under the load.

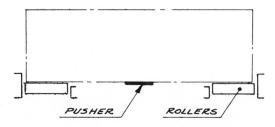

Fig. 14–12. Mechanical pusher for storage lane.

The pressure exerted by the slipping belt is very light. Normally a timing device will shut off the belt conveyor after it has traveled the length of the lane. The conveyor is automatically restarted whenever a load is removed from the lane or when a new load is inserted at the loading end. This arrangement assures that all loads will be advanced to the discharge end and prevents the conveyor or pusher from running after it has accomplished its purpose. A chain conveyor with a smooth flat top in contact with the loads may be substituted for the belt-type pusher.

Another form of a powered storage lane uses a live-roll conveyor, as shown in Fig. 14–13. In this arrangement the conveyor is automatically operated and shut off as described above for the mechanical pusher type.

Other types of pushers are used, but the belt and live-roll conveyor types are the most universal. Powered storage lanes, however, are seldom required for the average load. When it is desired to store pallet loads or similar heavy units, the powered type of lane is preferred to the gravity type.

All effort should be made to have cartons, boxes, etc., conveyed with the long dimension of the load in the direction of travel. All loads will then more readily stay in alignment while being accumulated. A rectangular load is sometimes stored with the long dimension across the width of the conveyor, but there is then a tendency for the load to skew as it travels down the gravity lane. To prevent this, the width of the lane

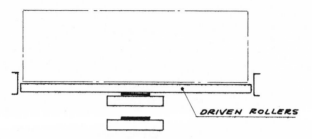

Fig. 14–13. Live-roller storage lane.

must be designed to give very little clearance over the load width. Racks so designed are not as readily modified to accommodate changes in package width.

Escapements

The type of escapement or stop used to automatically release an item from the storage lane depends on the character of the package, the frequency with which items are called out of the lane, and the type of takeaway conveyor arrangement. All escapements must be capable of ejecting a single item without interference from the other accumulated items.

LIGHT LOADS

Figure 14–14 shows various forms of simple escapements that can be used when very light packages (about one pound or less) are being handled. Such loads are frequently better adapted to the slide or chute type of rack.

In Fig. 14–14(a), the solenoid is energized when a package is to be ejected. The lever momentarily contacts the forward half of the bottom of the package and lifts it over the fixed stop. The pressure of the other accumulated packages forces the mass forward, and the first package rides free of the storage lane. A spring or counterweight quickly returns the lever to a position below the bed of the lane. Any other quick acting device may be used in place of the solenoid.

In Fig. 14–14(b), a retractable stop is lowered by the solenoid and quickly restored to the stop position. In this design the accumulated mass again pushes the released package free of the storage lane. The stop must return to its normal position before the next package reaches the lane unloading position. As a result the returning stop raises the back end of the ejecting package, but this does not deter the discharge of light loads.

In Fig. 14–14(c), the stop holds the line of accumulated loads. Here the solenoid or other actuator raises the stop and simultaneously applies a brake to the next package(s) in the mass. The released package is free to move from the lane by gravity. When it has cleared, the stop is low-

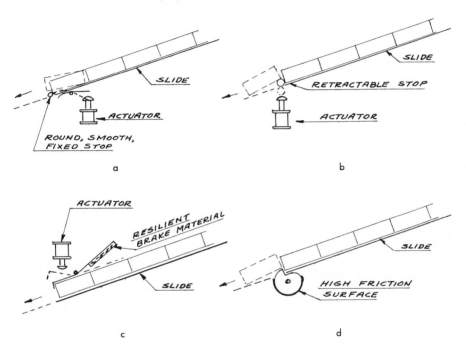

Fig. 14–14. Storage lane escapements.

ered, the brake is released, and the mass of accumulated loads moves forward to the stop. The frequency of successive releases is not as high as with the escapements shown in Fig. 14–14(a) or (b), but the released package is not lifted while being ejected. Obviously the package must be capable of withstanding the brake action.

In Fig. 14–14(d), a cam roller with a flat stop face and high-friction roll surface is caused to revolve one revolution at high speed. The length of the roll surface is about ⅔ the length of the package. While turning, the roll surface speeds the discharge of the ejecting package. The cam comes to rest before the following package has reached the stop face of the cam. This type of escapement can also be used for heavier loads in slide, wheel, or roller conveyor racks.

The above samples of simple escapement mechanisms may be of value to the engineer designing an automatic picking system. If the designs do not fully meet his needs, the illustrations may be helpful in developing an escapement that will be suitable.

HEAVY LOADS

When heavier loads (up to about 50#) are to be handled, the wheel or roller conveyor rack is normally used. The escapements must be of a sturdier design than those shown in Fig. 14–14, with the possible exception of the one shown in Fig. 14–14(d). Several designs are shown in Fig. 14–15.

In Fig. 14–15(a), a belt conveyor is made in two sections but with a common drive. The conveyor, when stopped, acts as an effective stop to hold back the accumulated loads. The last section of the conveyor operates at a speed at least twice that of the first section. Thus, when the conveyor is actuated to eject a package, the space between packages is increased materially. The first package is discharged and the conveyor stops to hold back the following loads.

In Fig. 14–15(b), a hinged section of roller conveyor is normally "up," and the first roller acts as a stop for the accumulated packages. When a package is to be discharged, the hinged section is lowered and held in the down position until about ⅔ of the package length has advanced. The hinged section is then returned to the up position and the ejected package continues to discharge, but the following packages are retained. It is always possible that the pressure of a long line of accumulated packages will be sufficient to impel the second package to "lift" with the first when it is raised by the hinged section. To prevent this from happening a restraining bar is sometimes installed above the second package position.

In Fig. 14–15(c), a pivotal arm with two rollers is held by a latch in the position shown. The upper roller acts as a stop for the accumulated packages. The section of conveyor holding the first package is graded at a steeper angle, and the discharge section is at a still greater angle. When the latch is momentarily released, the arm rotates and the released package moves ahead at a faster pace than do the following packages. The ejecting package tips on the steep grade, and the other roller on the rotating arm rises above the roller bed of the storage lane. The next package in the line of accumulated loads contacts the high roller and advances it to the stop position. The restored latch holds the arm until the next release impulse is received.

Again, the escapements shown in Fig. 14–15 are illustrative of the types that have been used. Other designs can be developed to meet specific requirements.

As mentioned previously, all escapements should assure complete control of the item being called out or ejected from the lane. They must be capable of separating the ejected item from others in storage. In all cases a counting signal is fed back to the master control to assure the removal

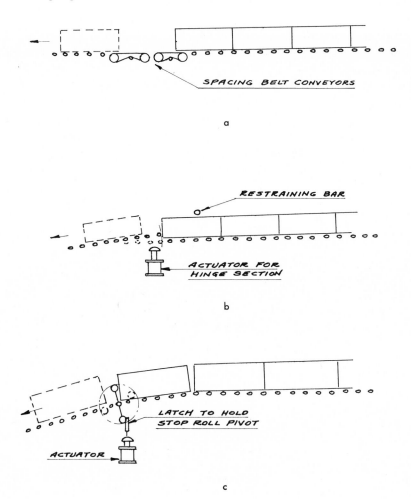

Fig. 14–15. Heavy-duty escapements.

of the correct number of items. In any high-speed operation, the escapements must be capable of releasing items at a rate of 40 or more per minute. Of the designs illustrated, those in Figs. 14–14(a) and (b) and 14–15(b) and (c) have the ability to release successive items quickly. The units in Figs. 14–14(d) and 14–15(a) operate at lower rates.

Takeaway Conveyors

CONNECTIONS

An important link in the operation of the automatic storage rack is the connection between the storage lane and the takeaway conveyor. The shape and type of package have a bearing on the design of the connection. Figure 14–16 illustrates a few basic connections. When the package length is up to 1.4 times the width, the transfer can be made directly via

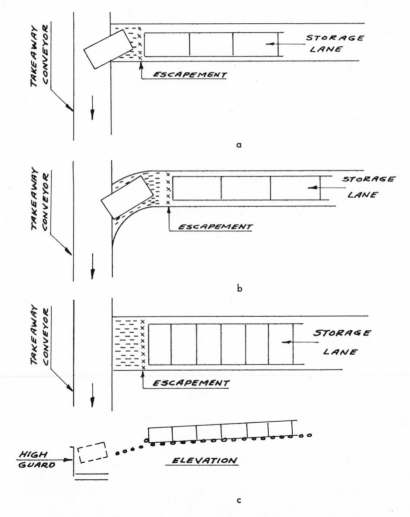

Fig. 14–16. Storage lane connections to takeaway conveyors.

a short straight conveyor, as shown in Fig. 14–16(a). If the package length is more than 1.4 times its width, a curved spur, as shown in Fig. 14–16(b), is required. When a package is stored which has a width greater than its length, the transfer is made by allowing the package to drop directly onto the takeaway conveyor, as shown in Fig. 14–16(c). In all of these connections the distance from the escapement to the takeaway depends on the kind of escapement used. Also, in some connections, as in Fig. 14–14(c), it may be necessary to have the package travel 12″ or more on the connecting conveyor to assure sufficient momentum to cause the package to "jump" rather than "fall" onto the takeaway.

All connections illustrated in Fig. 14–16 are shown as wheel conveyors. The wheels permit the package to attain greater speeds and to maneuver more readily than would roller conveyors. Rarely is power required in the connection. In transferring pallet loads or similarly heavy items from a storage lane to a takeaway conveyor, special powered units are required. In all such instances the rate of handling is low.

In most cases a takeaway conveyor is provided for each tier or level of storage lanes. In a few cases, where light loads of a non-fragile nature are handled, a single takeaway may serve to collect from two or more tiers. In the latter arrangements the items from the upper tiers fall onto the takeaway conveyor. One installation allows packages to drop five feet and operates very successfully.

RELEASE CONTROLS

The "takeaway" conveyor is normally a belt conveyor operating at sufficient speed to permit ejections at high speed. The items are released from the lanes in a programmed sequence to avoid interference in transferring to the takeaway. The sequence of picking will vary with the volume of flow; i.e., picking may start at the upstream lane or at the downstream lane. Another method is to scan the takeaway conveyor and allow a lane to discharge whenever a space is available on the conveyor. Still another assigns an area of the takeaway conveyor to each lane scheduled to discharge. When this area arrives at the proper spot, the lane discharges its complement of loads. The length of the area assigned is automatically selected for the number of items being released.

Picker Controls

There are many methods of controlling the picking operation. An operator stationed at a push-button console can depress the escapement button once for each item desired. Or the operator may set a "count," and then start the escapement in operation. The escapement will continue to function until the count has been satisfied. Still another method allows the operator to set up an entire order on the console. When the takeaway conveyor is clear, the operator releases the order. Each lane will eject its loads in the order set on the console. While the order is being picked, another order can be set up on the console as fast as the counting devices show "zero." This second order will not be released until the release button is again depressed by the console operator.

Fig. 14—17. Automatic order picking with picker stationed at console. (Courtesy Mathews Conveyer Company.)

Another method is to control the picking by punched cards or by punched or magnetic tape. With this method the orders are separated and programmed by card- or tape-processing machines. Very high picking rates are possible with the latter method.

Loading Storage Racks

All of the discussion in this chapter has been confined to types of racks, escapements, and methods of picking orders. The emphasis has been on removing items from the storage lanes. The stock in the lanes is replenished by manual operation. Normally the storage lane is equipped with a signaling device to warn when the number of pieces in the lane has reached an established minimum. Or, if two or more lanes have been assigned to a fast moving item, the signal indicates that a lane is empty. A pallet load is brought from the reserve stock and raised to the proper loading level, and the lane is replenished manually.

Automation of the loading operation is also possible. The reserve pallet loads can be stored in a storage rack. When a signal is received that stock is required, the proper pallet load moves out of the rack and is conveyed to an automatic pallet unloader. The individual items or packages are then conveyed to a feeding conveyor located at the tier level serving the loading end of the empty lane. A deflector or diverter automatically loads the empty lane.

It is possible in such an operation to have pallet loads picked up by lift trucks at the receiving dock and placed into a storage rack. The operations of loading the package storage racks, picking the items from these racks, and delivering them to the order-marshaling area or shipping dock are all performed by automatic equipment.

When punched cards or tapes are used to control the picking and possibly the rack-loading operations, inventory records, shipping bills, invoices, etc., can all be produced by the card- or tape-processing machines. In considering the merits of an automatic handling system, the savings in paperwork that are possible may be an influential factor in making a decision.

15

Conveyor Accessories

Many accessory mechanisms, such as brakes, diverters, positioners, transfers, turntables, etc., are combined with conventional conveyors to construct fully automated handling systems. Such accessories are also used in semiautomatic installations to perform functions not economically or readily performed by hand. Some units have warranted separate discussion in previous chapters. Other accessories frequently used are covered in this chapter.

Brakes

In this category are included mechanical brakes or conveyors used as stops, or combination conveyors that also serve as metering devices. The greatest need for stops and/or metering units is at the ends of accumulating lines. Roller, wheel, live-roll, and smooth-top chain conveyors are the types most often used to accumulate loads.

The first consideration in designing the brake is the magnitude of the force that will act against it. In Chapter 5, on roller and wheel conveyors, the pressure was given as about 2# for each 100# of live load. More complete factors are given in Table 15–1, which shows the force created by an accumulated load under various conditions and for different types of loads.

In Chapter 7, on live-roll conveyors, the formula is given for calculating the pressure created on these conveyors. It would be well to review the discussion on the different types of live-roll conveyors that can be used for accumulation.

The types of chain conveyors used for accumulation are illustrated in Fig. 8–12. The friction between the smooth flat surface of the chain and the package will vary from 30 per cent to 40 per cent. This percentage of the total accumulated mass will give the magnitude of the pressure developed. The chain type of accumulator is normally encountered in processing operations (packing, sealing, labeling, wrapping, etc.). In most cases the unit loads are very light, and the number of accumulated items is never very large. Therefore, the pressures developed are not very great even though the friction is relatively high.

Table 15–1. Factors for determining pressure exerted by accumulated loads.

Grade – Inches per Foot	Force in Pounds for Each 100 Pounds Live Load					
	Roller Conveyor			Wheel Conveyor		
	Carton		Wood or Metal Load	Carton		Wood or Metal Load
	Firm	Soft		Firm	Soft	
0.20"	–	–	–	1.0	–	1.3
0.30"	1.0	–	2.0	1.7	1.5	2.2
0.40"	2.0	1.7	2.8	2.6	2.3	3.0
0.50"	2.7	2.0	3.4	3.4	3.0	3.7
0.60"	3.4	2.8	4.0	4.2	3.6	4.6
0.70"	4.3	3.7	5.0	5.0	4.4	5.3
0.80"	5.0	4.4	5.8	5.8	5.3	6.1
0.90"	5.9	5.5	6.5	6.6	6.2	7.1
1.00"	6.8	6.2	7.1	7.5	7.2	8.0

Figure 15–1 shows some forms of simple stops. The mechanism in Fig. 15–1(a) consists of a plate that can extend the full width of the conveyor. The pressure is distributed over a comparatively large area. The force required to retract the stop is about 35 per cent of the total pressure. A modified form of plate or bar stop is shown in Fig. 15–1(b). Here the bar is pivoted to enable it to retract below the conveying bed. The effort to retract the stop is also 35 per cent of the pressure.

The roller stop in Fig. 15–1(c) can be retracted easily because the rolling friction is only about 2 per cent, but the entire force of the accumulated load is concentrated along the contact line of the roller, and the package is subjected to a high unit pressure.

All three of the above stops are used when the entire accumulated load is released and permitted to flow out. The stops are not adaptable to metering or flow control, unless applied to a live-roll conveyor where the driven rollers on the exit side of the stop can be driven much faster than those in the accumulating area. This difference in speed will space the loads so that the stop can be raised between them to control the flow.

Also, these stops are frequently manually operated when used in gravity conveyors where operators are performing other functions along the conveyor line.

The first roller in the hinged section of conveyor in Fig. 15–1(d) acts as a stop. The hinged section can be raised after each load has advanced

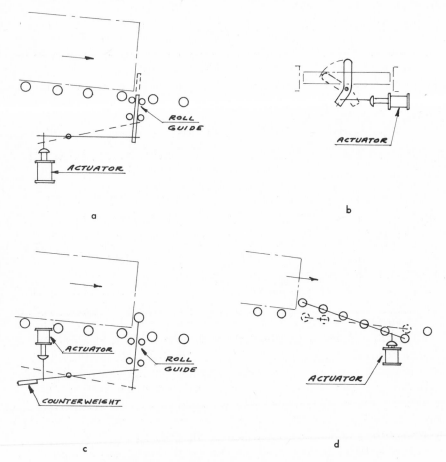

Fig. 15–1. Simple stops for gravity conveyors.

about ⅔ of its length beyond the stop roller. When this is done, the stop can control the number of loads released. All loads should also be of a reasonably uniform length to permit effective flow control.

In any of these stops, the first package or item resting against the stop must be capable of withstanding the pressure developed by the mass of accumulated loads. If the package is a carton, it is possible that it will resist serious damage to the outer casing but sustain damage to its contents. As an example, the carton may contain canned goods and be subjected to a heavy concentrated pressure along the contact line of a roller stop. The carton stock may be depressed by the roller without receiving permanent damage, but the cans in the carton may be likewise depressed. The carton stock will spring back after release from the stop but the cans are permanently damaged.

Short belt conveyors are frequently used as stops on accumulating lines. This type of stop prevents damage to fragile loads. The packages in the accumulator contact each other squarely, and the pressure is distributed over the entire end area of the package. The belt conveyor stops shown in Fig. 15–2 are long enough to accommodate sufficient packages to hold back the accumulated pressure by virtue of the friction between the belting and the packages on the stopped conveyor.

The length L required, with the conveyor equipped with a high-friction belt surface as used on inclined conveyors, can be calculated as follows:

$$L \text{ (feet)} = \frac{F \times 0.083\, Pl}{W \times v}$$

where

F = force in pounds of accumulated mass
Pl = length of individual package (inches)
W = weight in pounds of individual package
v = factor from Table 15–2

Table 15–2. Factors used in calculating conveyor lengths acting as stops for accumulated loads.

Arrangement of Stop Belt	Values of Factor v		
	Type of Package		
	Carton	Wood Case	Metal Pan
Declined 1/2" / foot	0.43	0.36	0.30
Horizontal	0.47	0.40	0.36
Inclined 1/2" / foot	0.51	0.44	0.40
Inclined 3/4" / foot	0.53	0.46	0.42
Inclined 1" / foot	0.55	0.48	0.44
Inclined 2" / foot	0.63	0.56	0.51
Inclined 3" / foot	0.72	0.65	0.58

The minimum length given by this formula should never be reduced. The conveyor should be arranged so that the plane of travel on the accumulator is maintained. This allows the packages to continue completely flat contact with each other. As the mass of accumulated loads increases, the package(s) on the stopped conveyor is pushed over the high-friction surface of the belting. The conveyor length is sufficient to prevent packages from being forced ahead and off the stopped conveyor when the maximum length has accumulated.

The belt conveyor stop, when arranged to decline the same as the gravity accumulator or when horizontal, as may be the case for a live-roll accumulator, will give maximum protection to the packages. If the live-roll conveyor is installed at a slight decline as discussed in Chapter 7, the belt conveyor stop can also be declined as for the gravity conveyor accumulator.

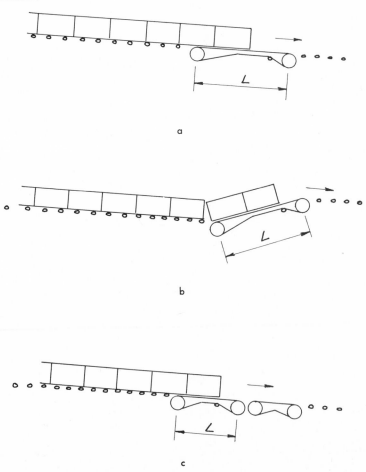

Fig. 15—2. Belt conveyor stops for gravity conveyors.

It will be noted that additional values for factor v are included in Table 15–2. These additional values should be used if the belt conveyor stop is arranged at an incline to permit using a shorter length L. When these arrangements are used, the packages are subject to pressure along the top edges as illustrated in Fig. 15–2(b).

An additional belt can be added ahead of the stop belt, as shown in Fig. 15–2(c). This additional belt is driven from the stop belt at a speed at least twice as fast as that of the stop belt. The packages will then be spaced as they are metered out, and a counting device can be incorporated.

Diverters

In addition to the various types of deflectors and diverters described for use with belt and with live-roll conveyors, there are units that can distribute loads, in any ratio, to two or more systems being fed from a supply conveyor line. One such unit is illustrated in Fig. 15–3. In this

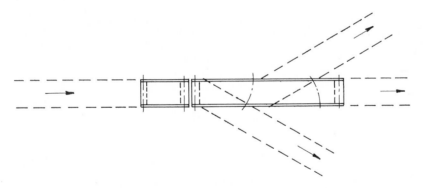

Fig. 15–3. Deflector-type diverter.

design, the flow from the supply line is metered and spaced on the two-section powered conveyor. If the flow from the supply line is, say, ten items per minute, three can be diverted to the right, four to the left, and three allowed to travel straight ahead to the third position. The ratio of diversions, as well as the number of diversions, is flexible (changes in ratio can be programmed to change at predetermined periods). In place of a two-section powered conveyor, the spacing and feeding of items to the diverting unit can be controlled by any form of escapement device.

The diverters need not be the deflector type shown in Fig. 15–3. The powered conveyor can be belt, live-roll, slat, or some other type. The diverters may be pushers that divert the items off at right angles to the conveyor. (See the discussion on transfers later in this chapter. The diverters may be one of the simple switches illustrated in Fig. 5–13, with remote controlled actuators to move the switch into the proper position.) Some form of spacing device should be employed to separate the loads

Fig. 15–4. Slat conveyor equipped with powered pushers to divert loads selectively to accumulating roller conveyor lines. (Courtesy Alvey-Ferguson Company.)

so that changes in the switch position can be made without interrupting the flow of loads through the diverter. Switch-type diverters can be used with belt and with live-roll conveyor systems as well as with gravity conveyors.

Positioners

A positioner can be any mechanical device used to orient the item being conveyed into a machine tool or to change its position while being conveyed; or, it may be some form of transfer which alters the position of the item while achieving the transfer. Figure 15–5 illustrates two common positioners used to reorient items as they advance on conveyor lines. Such devices are known as "upenders," "downenders," and "turnovers."

In the upper illustration in Fig. 15–5, a load traveling in the direction indicated is turned up on end for subsequent handling. If the flow direction is reversed, the load is downended as it passes through the positioner. Such units are commonly used in roller conveyor systems. The load is manually advanced to and placed into the positioner. The device is rotated and usually power-actuated, and the load is manually moved out and advanced. The same unit can be incorporated in an automatic system. The loads then would be spaced as they entered the positioner. The device would rotate, discharge its load, and return in time to receive the next approaching load.

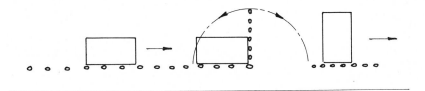

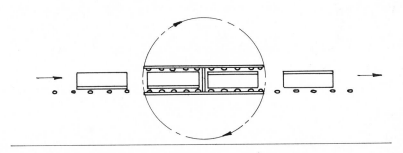

Fig. 15–5. Positioners for conveyor systems.

The above unit can be modified by using four arms of equal length in place of the long and short arms shown. With this modification the unit can continue to operate in one direction and so increase its handling capacity. Additional height is required, however, to allow clearance for the arms as they swing below the conveying level.

The unit illustrated in the lower diagram in Fig. 15–5 turns the load a complete 180° or "turns it over." In this design there is no need to reverse the positioner as is done in the other unit described above.

No attempt is made to illustrate or describe any of the many mechanical motions used to position items into and remove them from machine tools or other stations where operations are performed while the item is

Fig. 15–6. An upender on packing line operation. (Courtesy Lamson Corporation.)

being conveyed. Each such device is a specially designed mechanism adapted to the particular load being handled.

Transfers

In this grouping are included mechanisms that are better known as diverters, deflectors, positioners, or turntables. All of these units transfer material. Discussion here is confined to devices that the author feels cannot be classified otherwise.

TRANSFER CARS

A transfer car is a wheeled unit that mounts a section of conveyor. The conveyor may be a roller conveyor, level or declined, on which the load is temporarily held while the car is moved to another location for transfer of the load to a fixed conveyor line. A typical layout is shown in Fig. 15–8(a). All of the conveyor lines may be level, or they may be graded to or from the aisle served by the transfer car. The car may be moved from a conveyor line to another by manual effort, or it may be equipped with a powered drive. If the car conveyor or any of the other conveyor

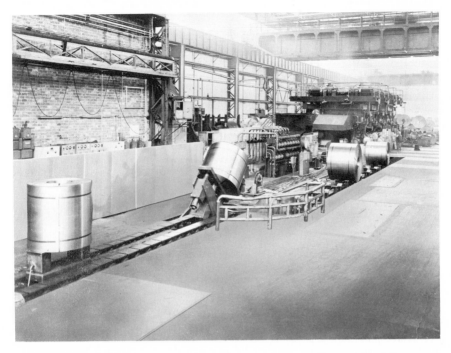

Fig. 15–7. Upender and flat-top chain conveyor handling coils of flat metal. (Courtesy Rex Chainbelt Inc.)

lines is graded, a hinged or retractable stop is provided to retain the load until the car is aligned with a line for transfer. The stop generally used for this purpose is shown in Fig. 15–1(b).

When the transfer car is equipped with a powered conveyor it is usually because the entire operation is automated. Power conveyors may be required also, if the loads are too heavy to be moved by manual effort. The operation in this latter case may not be fully automatic; an operator may walk with the car to control its movement and to start the power conveyor on the car when a transfer is to be made.

Transfer cars have been equipped with turntable tops when the direction of travel of the load requires the turning operation. The table usually is rotated while the car is moving between stations.

ELEVATING CHAIN AND WHEEL TRANSFERS

A transfer may consist of a chain conveyor mounted in a live-roll conveyor to effect transfer or diversion of heavy loads from and to the live-roll conveyor. Such an arrangement is shown in Fig. 15–8(b), where a two-strand chain conveyor is installed in the live-roll conveyor between the

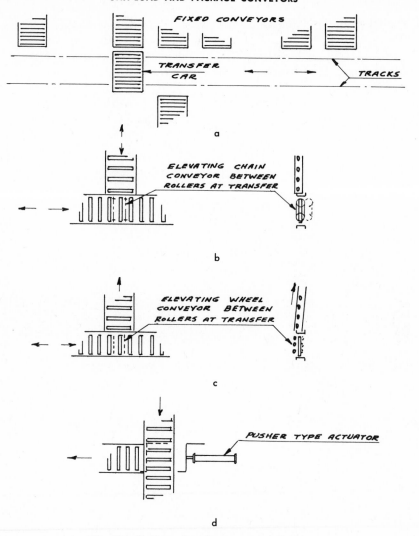

Fig. 15—8. Transfers for conveyor systems.

conveyor rollers. The normal position of the chains is below the live-roll conveying bed. When a load is registered over the chain conveyor, the chain conveyor raises and lifts the load off the rollers. At the same time the chain conveyor advances the load to a conveyor at right angles to the live-roll conveyor. Obviously, by reversing the sequence of operation, a load can be received from the side conveyor and deposited onto the live roll. Vee belts may be used in place of chains, at times.

A modified version of the above transfer is shown in Fig. 15–8(c). Here, in place of a chain conveyor between the rollers, a series of wheels or short rollers is mounted on a frame. When the load registers over this lift section, the wheels are raised to lift the load off the live roll. The wheels or rollers in the lift section are mounted at a grade. When elevated, the load moves forward by the force of gravity to deliver to the side conveyor.

PUSHERS

Another form of transfer uses a pusher that forces the load off the conveyor at right angles to its normal travel. Such an arrangement is shown in Fig. 15–8(d). The main conveyor can be a live-roll or slat conveyor. Belt conveyors can be used, but should be used with care because some loads may tend to pull the belting out of alignment. When the load registers opposite the receiving conveyor, an actuator is energized and pushes the load off, onto the receiver. If the main conveyor is live-roll, some form of stop is raised between the rollers to arrest the forward motion of the load during the transfer. If the main conveyor is slat or

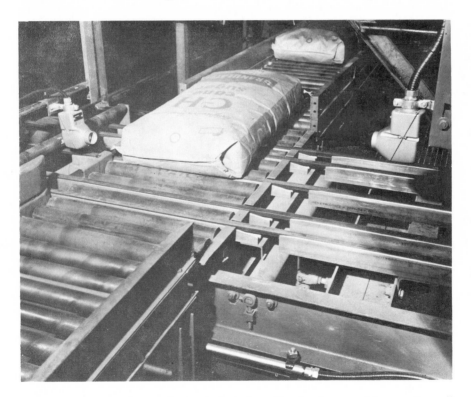

Fig. 15–9. Transfer employing belts in handling loads to and from a live-roll conveyor. (Courtesy Lamson Corporation.)

belt, the forward motion of the load is halted by a lip on the pusher ram that engages and holds the load while it is being transferred. The pusher may be motivated by a pneumatic or hydraulic cylinder, or it may be powered by an electric motor drive.

Turntables

Conventional turntable designs are used to effect transfer of loads from a main conveyor to one or more receiving conveyors. The tables can be used with any type of conveyor system employing roller, live-roll, belt, slat, or drag-chain conveyors. The turntable may mount a section of roller conveyor or may be equipped with a power conveyor. In the latter

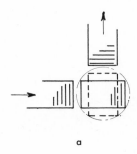

a

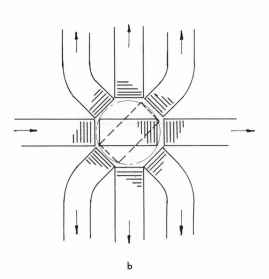

b

Fig. 15–10. Turntables for conveyor systems.

case the conveyor is usually of the same type as is used in the conveyor system. The operation may be a simple 90° turn, as illustrated in Fig. 15–10(a), or it may serve several conveyor lines at various angles, as in Fig. 15–10(b). The turning of the table can be by manual effort or the entire operation can be automated. If it is automatic, preselected loads may be dispatched to any of the receiving conveyors. The degree of turn; the stopping, transferring, and starting operations; the direction of the conveyor on the table; and the return of the table to the original position can all be automatically controlled.

Fig. 15–11. Automatic turntables distributing loads to warehouse areas. (Courtesy Lamson Corporation.)

The turning of the table may be actuated by an electric motor, or it may be operated by pneumatic or hydraulic cylinders. If cylinders are used and several degrees of turn are required, i.e., 45° and 90°, as indicated in Fig. 15–10(b), it is possible to use two cylinders. The stroke of one is exactly half the stroke of the other cylinder. Another method is to use one cylinder with sufficient stroke to rotate the table 90° and then insert a 2:1 reduction in the drive. The rotation is then reduced to 45° when desired. The use of a cylinder drive is an economical means of accomplishing exact registration with the various conveyor lines.

16

Controls for Automatic Operation

This chapter will review the various means available for controlling the automatic handling of items on a conveyor system. In many instances the area where an action is to take place is in a remote location or in a confined space where it is impractical to perform the operation manually. Automatic control may be needed not only to mechanize a manual function but also to automate a mechanical operation.

If punched cards, punched tape, or magnetic tape-processing equipment is available, it can usually be expanded to aid in programming the flow of material on the conveyor system. The method chosen to guide or control the flow will be influenced by the type of "paperwork" processing equipment available, or by the type of equipment it is contemplated to install.

In choosing the type of electrical control equipment, the rate of operation is also an important consideration. In any high-speed operation, the various parts will be required to function millions of times in a year. It may be desirable to use static control equipment rather than the conventional make-and-break contactors, to avoid costly down periods while repairs or replacements are being made. Static control is recommended where contaminated atmospheric conditions prevail, especially if the controls include sensitive relays or other contactors that require fast responses.

Operating units such as motors, solenoids, pneumatic and hydraulic cylinders, etc., also must be chosen for long life in high-speed operations. Cycles as small as 20 per minute result in over 2,000,000 operations annually for each 8-hour shift.

Coding

In any handling system, some or all of the following operations are encountered:

1. Counting
2. Segregation
   a. For quality control
   b. By size, shape, or weight
   c. By color
   d. For storage or shipment
3. Converging
4. Positioning

CODING LOADS

Probably the most economical procedure to aid in controlling the flow of material is to code the items being handled. When practical, the code should be applied to the load. If a carton or other container is being handled, identifying spots can be imprinted using a binary code. Many combinations are possible if spots are placed at different levels from the base of the load and at varying distances from the leading edge—in the direction of travel. Color coding of imprinted spots can also be used to increase the number of combinations.

If printing of spots is not possible, consider one of the following: spots may be sprayed on; reflective tape may be applied; or staples may be inserted in the outer casing of the carton or container.

When spots are located at various levels, the same code array can be used at the different levels. Scanners are located at corresponding levels so that any set of scanners will act only on the code at that level.

Additional combinations are possible by arranging the spots at varying distances from the leading edge of the load. The trigger switch in this arrangement is located at corresponding distances from the scanners. Since the scanners do not read the code until the trigger switch is actuated by the front of the load, they will only act on the loads when the spots register with the arrangement of scanners and trigger.

The procedure is the same when reflective tape is used in place of printed or sprayed spots.

When metal staples are used in place of spots, the location of the staples on the load can be as described above for spots. In place of scanners, electric brushes are used. The staples contact the brushes, and an electrical circuit is completed.

Obviously, trigger switches are not required if only one spot or staple is located at each level or when only a few separations are required. However, the type of action usually requires that the load be deflected or diverted from the conveyor in some manner. In most operations of this type it is imperative that the load be positioned properly when the action is taking place. A trigger switch assures the proper position for action.

CODING TOTES

If it is impossible to apply a code directly to the load, try to convey the load on a pallet, in a tray, or in some other kind of tote. If this can be done, the code can be applied directly to the tote or placed on a card that is then attached to the tote. In addition to spots or staples, magnetic tabs can be attached to or molded into the tote (plastic totes are normally used). Polarity patterns are "written" on the tabs, and "readers" interpret the code for action.

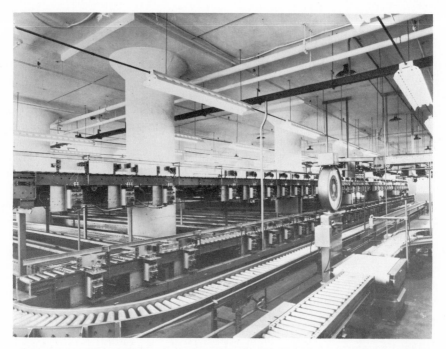

Fig. 16–1. Right-angle transfer stations for diverting loads from a feeding conveyor to accumulating lines. Here a coded tote leads a group of following uncoded loads to a selected storage line. (Courtesy Alvey-Ferguson Company.)

Another system uses totes equipped with flags or tabs that can be located or flipped into operating position at various locations across the top or down the sides of the tote. These tabs, upon reaching the designated station, actuate switches to trigger the action. The switches can be simple hatchway limit switches.

A common modification of this latter arrangement is to use a pallet or tote capable of containing several packages. In this way multiple loads can be dispatched using only one coded tote.

A tote equipped with any form of code can be used to dispatch a group of loads to any station in the conveying system. The first load is placed in a tote, or a dummy car or tote is coded for the destination, where we will assume a deflector is moved across the path of the conveyor. All following uncoded loads in the group are deflected at the station. The deflector remains across the conveyor in an operating position, until the leader tote of another group cancels the signal and continues on its way to another station.

CODING CONVEYOR ELEMENTS

It is possible that the load cannot be coded and that neither totes nor pallets can be used. However, it may be possible to code the conveyor elements. The cars of overhead trolley conveyors; the trays, pans, or cars of car-type chain conveyors; the cars of reciprocating or continuous vertical conveyors; the trucks on tow conveyors; the carriers in pneumatic conveyors, etc., can all be equipped with some form of identifying device. Usually flags or magnetic tabs are used in coding the conveyor elements. (See Chapter 12 for coding systems used with pneumatic conveyors.)

Belting is made with metallic elements introduced into the body of the belt. A code is "written" on the elements in the area below the load. Readers identify the code and trigger the action at the designated station. A belt conveyor can then be used with the same effectiveness as the various conveyors having cars, pans, or trays.

In any system where the code is indicated on a conveyor element, it is necessary to transfer the code automatically every time the load is transferred to another conveyor en route to its destination.

In any other system where the load or a tote is coded, the number of conveyor transfers and the time consumed in making the transfers is immaterial. Any variety of conveyors can be used in the system. The coded load or tote will be acted upon when it arrives at the designated station, regardless of elapsed time from dispatch or the sequence of its arrival at the station. The only requirement is that sufficient space be available between loads to permit proper operation of the action device. It may be necessary to provide a respacing unit ahead of the station where the action takes place.

Sequential and Timing Control

When coding of the load, tote, or conveyor element is impossible, the flow of the loads in the system can be controlled by memory devices using sequential or timing means of operation.

If sequential control is used, transfers between conveyors can be gravity-type, but arrangements must be made to keep loads from passing each other and upsetting the sequence. Sequential control is impractical if there is any possibility that loads can be removed from or inserted into the system between the dispatch station and the action station.

If timing control is used, the type of conveyor and the kinds of transfers used between conveyors are of prime importance. The use of any type of gravity-operated conveyor should be avoided. This includes even short

Fig. 16–2. Control panel at dispatch station on selective conveyor for automatic delivery to accumulating storage lines. (Courtesy Alvey-Ferguson Company.)

gravity connections between powered conveyors. Live-roll conveyors should be used only when the load is soft enough to have high frictional contact with the driven rollers and when the rate of handling is not in excess of about 20 loads per minute.

Belt conveyors with generous drive pulley diameters and a proper snubbing arrangement to avoid slip between the belting and the pulley, and/or chain conveyors with sprocket or caterpillar drives are preferred for systems where timing control of load flow is used. Connections between conveyors should be powered to assure measured movement of the load. Conveyors should not be inclined or declined at or near the critical angles.

In any timing control it is essential that the code be maintained in the event of power failure or if the conveyors are momentarily stopped for any reason.

Timing devices are available for use where the dispatch station and the action station are incorporated in a single conveyor. (Some successful systems have been installed with multiple conveyors and powered connections when the total distance between stations was less than 500'.) These timing devices do not employ electronic memory means. The devices consist of a wheel or a miniature conveyor, driven from the conveyor at a reduced speed—for example, a ratio of 100:1 or more.

If the conveying medium is a belt conveyor, the timing device should be driven from an idler shaft to assure exact timing with the speed of the belting. Some devices are driven by frictional contact with the belting. A drive from the head shaft does not insure against a possible slip between the drive pulley and the belting. If the conveying medium is a sprocket- or caterpillar-driven chain conveyor, the timing device may be driven from any shaft-mounting sprockets—drive or idler.

Pins, knobs, or other small elements are placed on the timing device when the load is ready for dispatch. At a speed ratio of 100:1, every 1' of travel on the wheel or miniature represents 100' of load travel on the conveyor. The first action of the pin element on the moving timing device is to contact a switch that releases the load at the dispatch station. When the pin has advanced on the timing unit a distance that indicates the load has reached the action station, the pin contacts a switch that triggers the action.

Some of these devices hold the pins or other elements by magnetic force; others have indents that receive and hold the element. The pin can be manually placed on the timing device, or it can be automatically placed when the dispatcher presses a button on a console to designate the load's destination.

When the load is released at the dispatch station, a slight slip of the moving conveyor under the load may occur. Also, if the load is transferred between conveyors, some additional slip may occur. For these reasons the timing is not exact enough to permit handling rates in excess of about 20 loads per minute. With this rate and with a recommended conveying speed of no less than 120 FPM, the loads will be spaced about 6'-0" on centers. If the average load is 24" long, the spacing between loads will be 4'-0". This spacing will allow for the slight displacement of the load from the theoretical position on the conveyor when it arrives at the action station.

Counting

Loads must be separated so that they can be counted. The counting or registering of each item may not be solely for the purpose of totaling the production, but may also be required to permit automation of subsequent operations. A good example of this requirement is given in the discussion of the pallet loader operation in Chapter 13.

Loads can be separated in several ways. One method that can be used with any character of load is the two-conveyor unit in which the spacer operates at a greater speed than does the feeder section, as shown in Fig. 16–3(a).

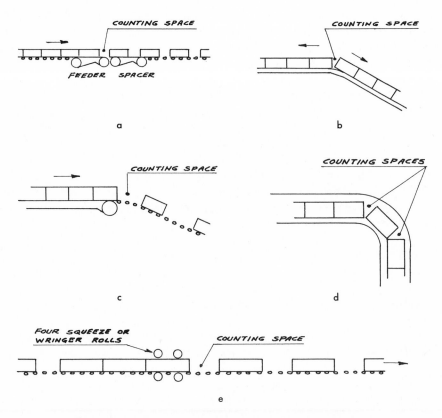

Fig. 16–3. Conveyor arrangements to permit counting.

In Fig. 16–3(b), a means is shown to separate the tops of rigid loads on a belt conveyor when it is not desirable to increase the spacing between loads. A similar condition can be obtained with the arrangement of a power conveyor and a positive gravity discharge as shown in Fig. 16–3(c).

In Fig. 16–3(d) the plan view of a gravity roller or wheel curve is shown. When rigid items (cartons, boxes, etc.) negotiate the curve, a counting space is opened at the outer edge of the curve.

When round loads are conveyed standing on end on the conveyor, the round shape provides a natural open counting space even when the round loads are contacting each other.

There are many possible modifications of these basic arrangements, especially the two-speed unit shown in Fig. 16–3(a). It is possible that when firm loads of a uniform height or width are being conveyed, they can be readily spaced by passing them through a set of "wringer" rolls as shown in Fig. 16–3(e). In this arrangement, four rubber-covered wringer rolls operate at a speed dictated by the rate at which the loads are to be handled. The power conveyor (in this illustration a live-roll) is operating at a speed at least 1.5 times the speed required by the handling rate. Assume that ten 24″ loads are required per minute. The surface speed of the wringer rolls is 20 FPM while the conveyor speed can be 30 FPM or faster.

Segregation

QUALITY CONTROL

As loads are being handled on a production line, they may be scanned to cull out all rejects, or, as in the case of filling operations, they may be scanned to detect the presence of foreign matter. When the scanning is automatic, it is usually done with the aid of the photoelectric eye. Photoelectric controls can operate at high speed—20 operations per second or greater—and they can detect minute objects that are in the light beam for only a small fraction of a second. This high speed and the need for detecting minute objects is seldom encountered in package material-handling. The capabilities, however, indicate why the photoelectric control has been used so successfully in controlling the flow of items at the relatively slow speeds employed.

The photoelectric eye can detect differences in colors and degrees of shade in the same color. It can detect temperature ranges so that processing conveyors may be speeded or slowed as needed. It is sensitive to changes in reflected light and is used to reject items improperly finished.

A weighing scale can be included in the conveyor bed to reject packages over or below the required weight. The weighing units are frequently used to control the amount of material entering the container at a filling operation.

SIZE, SHAPE, OR WEIGHT

When a conveying line handles loads of many sizes, they may be separated and diverted from the conveyor by differences in height, width, length, weight, or any combination of any two or all four of these dimensions. When these combinations are used, various shapes can be separated.

If loads are being separated by height only, and if they can be permitted to contact a switch lever, the simple hatchway limit switch can be used. The normal procedure is to divert the highest load first, then the next highest, and so on. When limit switches are used, a series of sensitive levers can be arranged to operate the switches for height variations of about plus or minus ½". When closer tolerances are required or when the load cannot be contacted, a photoelectric eye can be used to detect first the highest load and then, successively, the shorter loads.

Similar means can be employed to segregate loads by width. All loads are made to contact one guardrail of the conveyor. The widest load is detected first and then the narrower loads as before.

Separation by length variation can be accomplished by combining a timing device with the limit switch or the photoelectric eye. The length of time that the switch is contacted or the light beam interrupted indicates the load length. The longest load is detected first, followed by the shorter loads as was done for variations in height or in width. The timer at each station is adjusted to trigger the action when the timer has run for a predetermined time.

In all three of the above means of measuring differences in load sizes, the tolerances that are possible may not satisfy requirements. When extremely close differences must be detected, a code of some type should be used. A code will permit separation of loads with only slight size differences, and of course it can detect loads of the same size that require segregation because of differences in their contents.

When loads are to be separated by weight differences, it is usually done by inserting a weighing scale in the conveyor. Scales are readily incorporated into roller or wheel conveyors, belt conveyors, or live-roll conveyors. They can also be inserted in chain conveyors, including the overhead trolley conveyor. Scales in chain conveyors, however, are normally limited to the handling of reasonably heavy loads.

Converging

It is frequently necessary to converge several conveyor lines into one transport conveyor. If it is desired to connect a manufacturing division with a storage or shipping area, it is usually more economical to converge all production lines into one conveyor for transport to a distant point. The separation of the various items from the transport conveyor has been discussed in this and previous chapters.

Converging of items can be accomplished in many ways. A typical arrangement is shown in Fig. 16–4. Several production lines are grouped in one area, and another line feeds into the collecting or transportation conveyor at a remote point.

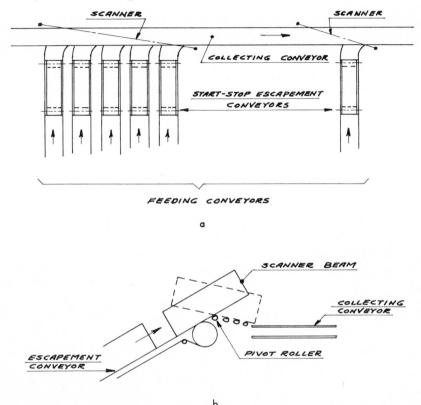

Fig. 16–4. (a) Converging arrangement for conveyor systems. (b) Transfer detail.

The feeding lines that are clustered at one point are controlled similarly to a series of lanes feeding from a storage rack. The start-stop conveyors, which act as escapements, may be operated in sequence to discharge one load each time they operate. The sequence may be arranged to start either upstream or downstream. It is also possible to have all escapements operate simultaneously and discharge one load from each line. A photoelectric eye scanner signals when the receiving area is clear, and the escapements can then discharge another group of loads.

The program selected for discharge to the collector depends on several factors. If the feeding lines are closely spaced and the production rate from each line is the same, simultaneous discharge is usually the most practical arrangement. It is customary to have the frequency of discharge slightly greater than is indicated by the production rate. The loads on all lines may not arrive at the proper discharge position at the same time. When an escapement receives the signal to discharge, it will not operate if a load is not in the proper discharge position. A limit switch or a photoelectric eye at each escapement determines whether a load is in discharge position.

When the production rate varies greatly on the feeding lines, the program of discharge regulates the operation of the escapements accordingly. It is also possible that the feeding lines are widely spaced. When these conditions exist, the customary treatment of each junction would be similar to that for the arrangement for the one remote line, indicated in Fig. 16–4.

The single production line escapement is equipped with a reversing motor. A photoelectric eye scans the receiving area of the collecting conveyor for possible interference with oncoming loads. Another eye scans the end of the escapement to detect the position of any load on the escapement. The relation of the connection between the escapement and the collector is detailed in Fig. 16–4. The escapement conveyor normally runs continuously. The load balances over the pivot roller and is either under the control of the escapement conveyor or is free to gravitate onto the collecting conveyor. The scanner beam on the escapement is arranged to be broken just before the load is released from under the control of the escapement conveyor.

If a load interrupts the escapement scanner while another load is entering the scanner area on the collector, the escapement stops and retains its load until the collector is again clear. If the load is long and projects into the path of the collector while it is still on the escapement, the signal is received to stop the escapement, but this time the escapement is automatically reversed and pulls its load back out of the path of the collector.

There are many other arrangements possible, using start and stop automatic controls on powered conveyors. Also, mechanical devices are available to control "traffic" at an intersection. A mechanical device is adaptable for use with loads of reasonably rigid construction, uniform in size and in weight. Loads with small differences in size and weight will function well, as long as they can withstand contact with the mechanical arms used with these units.

Other Control Equipment

Many other needs for control equipment are encountered in material-handling systems. A few examples follow.

Frequently a master control panel is required to permit an operator to coordinate the movement of material throughout the system. The control panel may be elevated to give the operator a clearer view of the system.

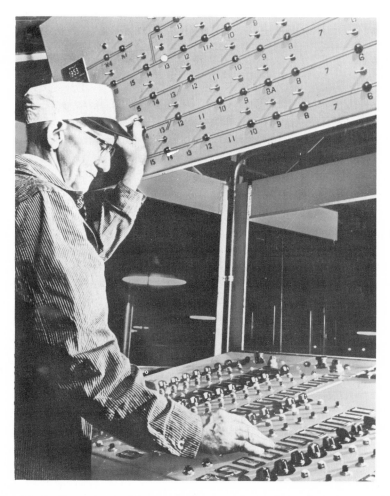

Fig. 16–5. Control panel for remotely operating system of conveyors. (Courtesy Lamson Corporation.)

Proper lighting is important. However, there may be areas that cannot be seen from the control area. These concealed areas can be equipped with cameras and a closed-circuit TV, to permit the operator to view the activity there.

Weighing scales can be equipped with measuring devices to record the volume of a package while it is being weighed. A tape shows length, width, height, and weight. In some cases the scale operator is provided with a push-button console whereby he can indicate, by code, other pertinent information such as destination, contents, etc. This type of information is needed in some operations where packages are received for assembly into outgoing shipments. In some terminal operations, the tape information received from the scale is fed to a computer which then advises the best assembly of loads to satisfy cube and weight limitations.

In any system of conveyors it is desirable to operate a conveyor at a speed in excess of the speed of the conveyor feeding it. This precaution will avoid jams. In addition, it is necessary to interlock the motor controls so that the feeding conveyor will stop automatically if the receiving conveyor shuts down for any reason. Audible or visual signals are frequently added to indicate such stoppages.

A very common condition occurs at the discharge of a powered conveyor when it delivers loads to a gravity, roller, or wheel conveyor for temporary storage. A limit switch or photoelectric beam combined with a timer is located in the gravity line near the discharge of the power conveyor. As loads pass the switch, the timer is actuated, but if the load is free to advance, the switch or photo beam is restored before the allotted time is exhausted. However, if the storage line is full, a load will remain at the switch and the timer will shut down the powered conveyor. The control wiring can be arranged to restart the power conveyor each time the safety switch is freed of a load. This results in frequent starts and stops of the power conveyor. A better arrangement is to allow the storage conveyor to divest itself of several of its stored loads and restart the power conveyor only when the number of loads in storage has been reduced to a desired minimum. The powered conveyor then will run until loads again back up to the safety switch. A second switch or eye is located at the minimum load point in the storage line.

Index